INFO Skills
BOOK FOUR

Skills for Life

INFO SKILLS
BOOK FOUR

Skills for Life

James McCafferty

Hodder & Stoughton
A MEMBER OF THE HODDER HEADLINE GROUP

Acknowledgments

The author and publishers would like to thank the following for permission to include copyright material in this book:

Argos Distributors Ltd for material from the Argos Spring/Summer 1995 catalogue (sheet 4); British Telecommunications plc for material from *the phone book* (sheet 5) and from the Bedford 1994/5 *Yellow Pages* (sheets 6, 7 and 8): YELLOW PAGES® is the registered trade mark of British Telecommunications plc in the United Kingdom, copyright reserved; BBC Publications for material from *Radio Times* (14-20 January 1995) (sheet 18); Teletext Ltd, London (sheet 19); British Rail and Trainlines of Britain, the official licensing and franchising operation of British Railways Board (sheets 23 and 24); The Automobile Association for material from the *AA Handbook* (sheets 25, 26, 27 and 29); and The Travel Club of Upminster, Station Road, Upminster, Essex RM14 2TT (sheet 33).

British Library Cataloguing in Publication Data
McCafferty, James
    Infoskills. – Book 4: Skills for life.
    1. Title
    025.524

ISBN 0 340 64326 9

First published 1996
Impression number   10 9 8 7 6 5 4 3 2 1
Year   1999   1998   1997   1996

Layouts by Bowberry House Design, Kent.
Printed in Great Britain for Hodder & Stoughton Educational, the educational publishing division of Hodder Headline Plc, 338 Euston Road, London NW1 3BH, by Redwood Books, Trowbridge, Wiltshire.

Contents

Introduction: A Note for Tutors

InfoSkills: A Guide for Users

Worksheets:

Through a broad cross-curricular range of learning assignments, **InfoSkills** aims to teach the key *process skills* which underpin the formal curriculum. The series takes the student through a carefully graded learning programme which develops the ability to *access* and *use* verbal and non-verbal information in a wide variety of contexts:

InfoSkills 1: Accessing Written Information
Contents: Alphabetical order. Using a dictionary. Using single-volume encyclopedias. Indexes. Guide words. Key words. Cross-references. Using multi-volume encyclopedias.

InfoSkills 2: Library and Research Skills
Contents: Looking for fiction books in a library. Using the Dewey system. Subject index. Using a contents page. Using an index. Reading for information. Using a thesaurus. Using the Guinness Book of Records. Using the Pears Encyclopaedia. Using a CD-ROM encyclopedia.

InfoSkills 3: Data Handling
Contents: Numerical order. Gathering, representing and interpreting information: graphs. Misleading graphs. Tables. Pie charts. Calendars. AD and BC. Temperature. Information from diagrams and pictures. Information from plans. Scale. Maps: regions and directions. Bearings. Using a world atlas. Grid references. Latitude and longitude. Contours and relief.

InfoSkills 4: Skills for Life
Contents: Everyday signs. Reading a meter. Shopping from a catalogue. Telephone directories. Yellow Pages. Telephone charges and bills. Eating out. Shopping on a budget. Seating plans. Getting organised. TV and teletext. Timetables. On the road. Handbooks and gazetteers. Planning a journey. Planning a holiday. Small ads. VAT. Discounts. Personal banking. Buying a car. Finding a job.

The age-focus of **InfoSkills** is deliberately wide. Primary classes will find some of the modules in *Accessing Written Information* and *Data Handling* appropriate for their needs, whilst secondary students will be able to tackle all the material. Those working towards 16+ qualifications will find the work in *Library and Research Skills* and *Data Handling* particularly helpful in reinforcing and practising the research skills essential for coursework. Students working on skills-based and vocational courses will find similar benefits, whilst students in the special needs sector can use *Accessing Written Information* and *Skills for Life* to good effect.

The coverage of the series is deliberately very wide, linking the progressive development of information skills to many of the formal subject areas which students will encounter at school and college.

	Key Stage Two (ages 7-11)	Key Stage Three (ages 11-14)	Key Stage Four (ages 14-16)	Special Education	Further Education (ages 16+)	GNVQ
Accessing Written Information	●	●		●		
Library and Research Skills	●	●	●		●	●
Data Handling	●	●	●		●	●
Skills for Life		●	●	●	●	●

The first two books in the series, *Accessing Written Information* and *Library and Research Skills*, lay the essential foundations of written information skills, beginning with simple work on alphabetical order and progressing through using dictionaries, encyclopedias, non-fiction books and other book-based information sources to the acquisition and application of more advanced research skills, including computer-based multimedia systems. These books work well alongside the formal English, History and Humanities curricula.

Book 3, *Data Handling*, takes the student through a wide range of data-handling assignments and ensures the effective development of non-verbal information skills. The student learns to handle charts, tables, graphs, diagrams, drawings, plans and maps. *Data Handling* reinforces and develops these essential skills alongside coursework in Mathematics, Geography, Personal and Social Education (PSE) and Humanities.

Book 4, *Skills for Life*, places students' development of information skills in an everyday context, confronting them with a range of real-life decision-making situations which require an understanding of the information systems which dominate our daily lives. *Skills for Life* is an extremely flexible resource, with assignments suitable for Key Stages 2 and 3 of the National Curriculum, secondary PSE courses and life skills programmes in Further Education and Special Education.

There is much to be gained from using the assignments in **InfoSkills** in sequence: the skills are arranged in ascending order of difficulty, each skill building on earlier foundations.

However, *flexibility* is a hallmark of the series. Accordingly, the work is arranged in modules, each dealing with a particular dimension of information skills and each with links to specific subject areas in the formal curriculum. For example, the data-handling material on graphs and pie charts has a strong mathematical emphasis, but the information which is presented links across to issues encountered in Humanities and PSE. Similarly, the reference skills in Books 1 and 2 are rooted in the English curriculum, but the subject matter used to practise the skills links across to History, Humanities, PSE and World Studies.

The photocopiable format of **InfoSkills** encourages the selective use of assignments to support coursework elements in the mainstream subject curriculum. In addition, the sheer breadth of the material provides a wealth of free-standing lesson opportunities for supply teachers and staff covering for absent colleagues. In many cases, the modular grouping of the tasks allows a linked sequence of assignments to be delivered over several days or weeks, avoiding the need for unrelated 'one-off' teaching sessions. The materials are ideally suited to the needs of students who have been disadvantaged by earlier years of inadequate skills teaching.

Finally, where **InfoSkills** is to form a significant element of students' learning activities, it is most important that they have the opportunity to understand and discuss what it is about. They need to know where they are and where they are going. For that reason, it is recommended that, wherever appropriate, the two pages of *InfoSkills: A Guide for Users* are copied and discussed with students before work begins.

InfoSkills: A Guide for Users

We live in an age in which vast amounts of information pass electronically from one side of the world to the other in seconds. The sheer volume of that information and the speed with which it can be transmitted have far outstripped our capacity to absorb or use more than a small part of it. The lights of the information superhighway are clearly visible, but it's rather as if we are travelling along an unlit country road which runs alongside a motorway. We can see where we want to be, but we can't find the access road which will take us onto it. Worse still, if we hit the right junction and find ourselves on the highway, we suddenly realise that we can't read the roadsigns or follow the directions. We're driving blind.

That's exactly the position most people are in most of the time. It's hard to find our way into the information fast lane and, even when we find it, we can't understand the signs that could help us plan our learning route. Small wonder, then, that most of us give up and opt for the guided coach tour instead. That way, we're in the safe hands of the driver and the tour guide, who know their way around (or at least they say they do). If we see a direction sign we don't understand, we can always ask them. Or better still, it's much easier to sit back and be driven wherever the tour guide decides to take us - all aboard for the mystery tour! We know we're on the move, but the journey is in someone else's hands. We don't know the route - or our destination - and after a while we learn not to care, because the tour guide knows where we are going, and that's all that matters. And if we are sometimes baffled by the roadsigns or puzzled by the sights and sounds that we pass, we can always ask. We can always rely on the guide, can't we?

InfoSkills takes a different view. It is based on the belief that people should be enabled to plan their own learning journeys and to decide for themselves the destinations they want to reach. That is only possible, of course, if they can (a) drive themselves, and (b) understand the roadsigns. **InfoSkills** is designed to teach you how to drive and to understand the roadsigns you will come across on the roads which approach the information superhighway. Once you've mastered the skills and understood the highway code, the direction you take is then up to you.

If you are using **InfoSkills** at school or college, you can use it alongside the main curriculum. It will help you get to grips with all the chunks of knowledge that get thrown at you, and it should help you to start finding things out for yourself. Don't expect the education system to do everything for you. Schools and colleges will give you all the answers you could ever want, but they usually forget to ask you what the questions were. You'll find plenty of questions in **InfoSkills**. They probably won't be the questions you might want to ask, but you'll soon find out how to find answers for yourself, instead of relying on someone else. After that, YOU can decide the questions you want to ask.

You probably hear the word 'access' a lot. It means finding your way into a building, onto a street or highway, into an information system. **InfoSkills** is designed to give you the access skills you need to help you understand and use all kinds of information: dictionaries, encyclopedias, non-fiction books, plans, diagrams, maps, charts, tables, directories, catalogues, CD-ROM, timetables, menus and so on. How you use your new skills will be up to you. But you can be sure of one thing: as your skills increase, so will your *confidence*! And confident learners always do better, because they're not afraid to try things out for themselves or take the occasional risk. They can read the direction signs well enough to follow an unfamiliar route on their own, while everyone else stays on the bus with the tour guide. And who can tell what they might find?

You're probably wondering whether you have to work though everything in the four books which make up the **InfoSkills** series. No, you don't. It depends on what skills you already have. If you have already mastered basic skills like alphabetical sequencing and using first, second and third letter order, why spend time doing them again? If you have no problems with using an encyclopedia index, don't plough through all the worksheets on it. The key thing is to decide what skills you *already have*, what skills you *need to acquire* and then plug into the worksheets which develop those

skills (but don't avoid a skill just because it looks a bit harder!).

If you prefer, there is no reason why you shouldn't work through the sheets in order. They're arranged in each book so that the basic skills come first, with each new skill built on the earlier ones. That way, your grasp of information skills is developed gradually, a step at a time. Some schools and colleges will want to structure things in that way, so that your skills are built up alongside your main curriculum courses. That's fine.

And finally, if you want, you can just 'dip in' to **InfoSkills**, to work on a skill you're not so good at. You could use the Contents pages as a kind of checklist, to keep track of the skills you've been working on.

The important thing to remember is that **InfoSkills** is designed to put you, the learner, in charge. The more you are able to cut out the intermediaries (the tour guides), the more confident you will become and the more active you can be in your own learning. The job of **InfoSkills** is to teach you how to drive the information vehicle yourself, to understand the rules of the road and to read the direction signs. Once you can do all that, the information highway is all yours. Use it well!

James McCafferty

1 Look at the picture on sheet 1.1. There are **ten** things wrong. Look carefully at the signs in the picture and make a list of what is being done wrong:

2 What do these everyday signs mean?

(a) **P** _____

(b) *i* _____

(c) _____

(d) _____

(e) _____

(f) _____

(g) At any time _____

(h) _____

(i) TOILETS _____

(j) _____

How much electricity do you use?

Every house uses electricity to run things like kettles, fridges, TVs and so on. Lots of houses also use electric cookers and electric heating systems. So it's very important to know how much electricity you are using, because you have to pay for it!

Electricity is measured in **units** called **kilowatt hours** (kWh): using one kilowatt of electricity for one hour uses up one unit.

An ordinary light bulb is usually 100 watts. An electric fire is often at least 1 kilowatt.

There are 1,000 watts in one kilowatt

Work out the missing numbers so that each answer comes to one unit of electricity (1,000 watts used for one hour):

1 100w 100w 100w 100w 100w 100w 100w 100w 100w 100w X [1] hour = one unit

2 100w 100w 100w 100w 100w X [2] hours = one unit

3 100w X [ ] hours = one unit

4 1kw X [1] hour = one unit

5 2kw X [ ] hour = one unit

6 500w X [ ] hours = one unit

7 3kw X [ ] minutes = one unit

8 2000w X [ ] minutes = one unit

9 1000w X [ ] minutes = one unit

10 200w X [ ] hours = one unit

Reading an electricity meter

You can keep track of how much electricity you use at home by understanding how to read the **electricity meter**. Each time you switch on a kettle or vacuum cleaner or some other electrical appliance, the meter records how much power you are using. Then, once every **quarter** (every three months), the electricity company will send you an electricity bill which is worked out like this:

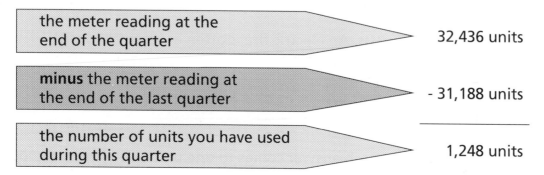

the meter reading at the end of the quarter — 32,436 units

minus the meter reading at the end of the last quarter — - 31,188 units

the number of units you have used during this quarter — 1,248 units

There are two main kinds of electricity meter in use. Most newer homes have the latest type of **digital meter**, which looks like this:

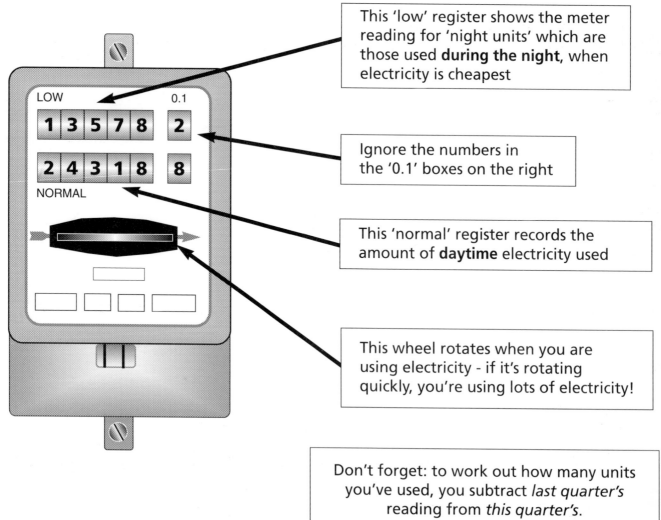

This 'low' register shows the meter reading for 'night units' which are those used **during the night**, when electricity is cheapest

Ignore the numbers in the '0.1' boxes on the right

This 'normal' register records the amount of **daytime** electricity used

This wheel rotates when you are using electricity - if it's rotating quickly, you're using lots of electricity!

Don't forget: to work out how many units you've used, you subtract *last quarter's* reading from *this quarter's*.

Use a calculator to help you work out how much electricity these meters have recorded this quarter. Work out how much the bill would be if these readings were **night units** at **3.6p** per unit or if they were **day units** at **9.25p** per unit. (Give your answer to the nearest penny.)

	Last quarter	This quarter	Units used	Night units cost	Day units cost
1	2 4 3 1 8	2 4 9 3 6		£	£
2	3 6 7 2 5	3 7 9 4 2		£	£
3	6 5 2 2 0	6 6 7 8 6		£	£
4	4 8 0 1 2	5 1 3 0 5		£	£
5	7 6 5 2 6	7 7 8 3 9		£	£

Some older homes still have **dial meters**, which look like this:

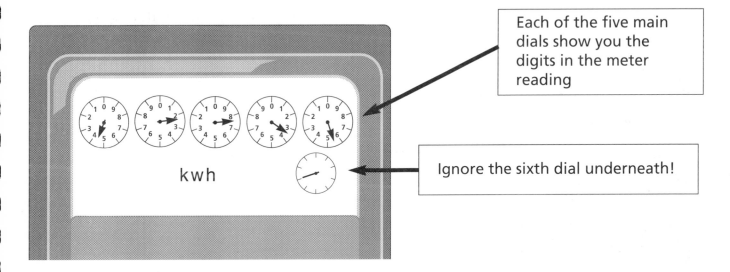

Each of the five main dials show you the digits in the meter reading

kwh

Ignore the sixth dial underneath!

You read each dial from 0, reading round the dial in the direction of the numbers (0, 1, 2, 3, ...)

If the pointer is **between** two numbers on the dial, you write down the number which the pointer has **just passed** (the smaller one), like this:

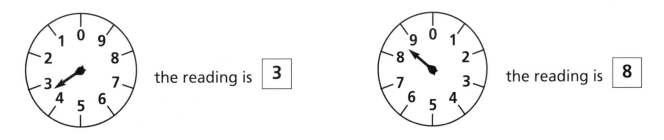

the reading is 3

the reading is 8

Write down these readings in numbers

6  ⬜

8  ⬜

7  ⬜

9  ⬜

Now write down the total number of units used this quarter:

10

⬜

11

⬜

12

⬜

Shopping from a catalogue

Although mail-order catalogues have been around for many years, the items you order may take several weeks to arrive through the post. Argos Stores were the first company to introduce store shopping based on a catalogue. Ordering at Argos is simpler because once you've paid for what you want, you collect it from a 'collection point'. Argos Stores also have many of their catalogue items on display, so you can see what they look like.

In the catalogue, each item has a catalogue number and price, together with a photograph of the product and a description, like this:

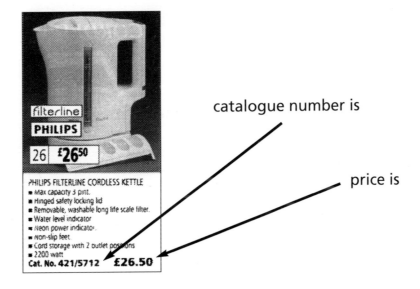

catalogue number is

price is

To order the items you want, you fill in an order form like this:

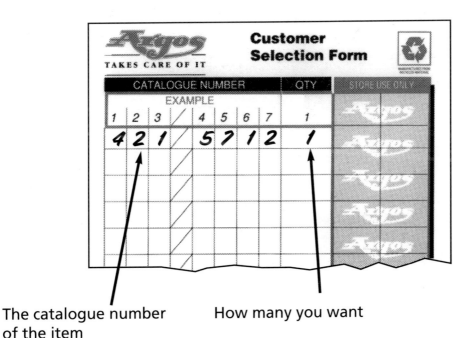

The catalogue number of the item

How many you want

Here are some of the electric toasters which appeared in the Spring/Summer 1995 Argos catalogue:

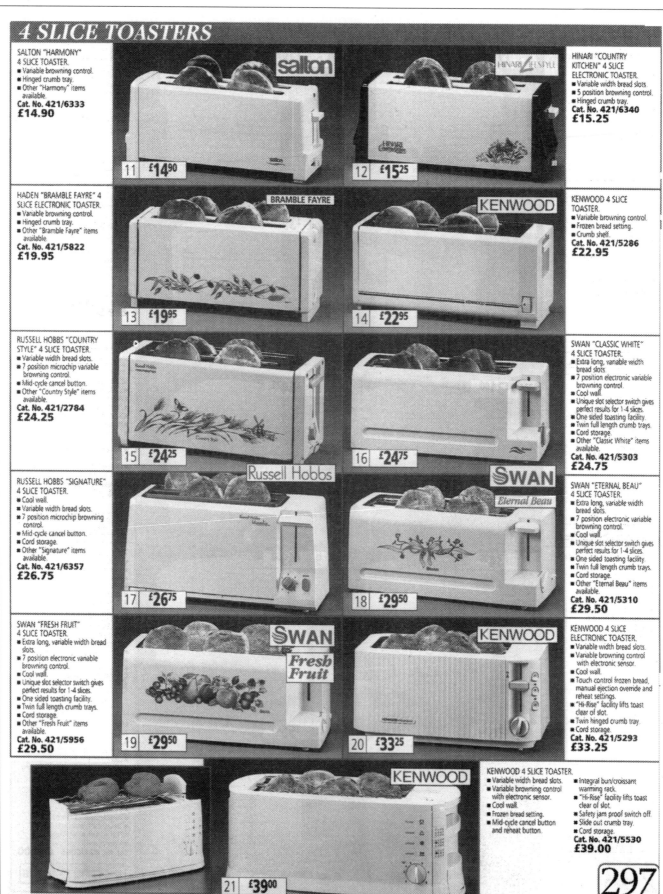

4 SLICE TOASTERS

SALTON "HARMONY" 4 SLICE TOASTER.
- Variable browning control.
- Hinged crumb tray.
- Other "Harmony" items available.
Cat. No. 421/6333
£14.90
11 £14⁹⁰

HINARI "COUNTRY KITCHEN" 4 SLICE ELECTRONIC TOASTER.
- Variable width bread slots.
- 5 position browning control.
- Hinged crumb tray.
Cat. No. 421/6340
£15.25
12 £15²⁵

HADEN "BRAMBLE FAYRE" 4 SLICE ELECTRONIC TOASTER.
- Variable browning control.
- Hinged crumb tray.
- Other "Bramble Fayre" items available.
Cat. No. 421/5822
£19.95
13 £19⁹⁵

KENWOOD 4 SLICE TOASTER.
- Variable browning control.
- Frozen bread setting.
- Crumb shelf.
Cat. No. 421/5286
£22.95
14 £22⁹⁵

RUSSELL HOBBS "COUNTRY STYLE" 4 SLICE TOASTER.
- Variable width bread slots.
- 7 position microchip variable browning control.
- Mid-cycle cancel button.
- Other "Country Style" items available.
Cat. No. 421/2784
£24.25
15 £24²⁵

16 £24⁷⁵

SWAN "CLASSIC WHITE" 4 SLICE TOASTER.
- Extra long, variable width bread slots.
- 7 position electronic variable browning control.
- Cool wall.
- Unique slot selector switch gives perfect results for 1-4 slices.
- One sided toasting facility.
- Twin full length crumb trays.
- Cord storage.
- Other "Classic White" items available.
Cat. No. 421/5303
£24.75

RUSSELL HOBBS "SIGNATURE" 4 SLICE TOASTER.
- Cool wall.
- Variable width bread slots.
- 7 position microchip browning control.
- Mid-cycle cancel button.
- Cord storage.
- Other "Signature" items available.
Cat. No. 421/6357
£26.75
17 £26⁷⁵

18 £29⁵⁰

SWAN "ETERNAL BEAU" 4 SLICE TOASTER.
- Extra long, variable width bread slots.
- 7 position electronic variable browning control.
- Cool wall.
- Unique slot selector switch gives perfect results for 1-4 slices.
- One sided toasting facility.
- Twin full length crumb trays.
- Cord storage.
- Other "Eternal Beau" items available.
Cat. No. 421/5310
£29.50

SWAN "FRESH FRUIT" 4 SLICE TOASTER.
- Extra long, variable width bread slots.
- 7 position electronic variable browning control.
- Cool wall.
- Unique slot selector switch gives perfect results for 1-4 slices.
- One sided toasting facility.
- Twin full length crumb trays.
- Cord storage.
- Other "Fresh Fruit" items available.
Cat. No. 421/5956
£29.50
19 £29⁵⁰

20 £33²⁵

KENWOOD 4 SLICE ELECTRONIC TOASTER.
- Variable width bread slots.
- Variable browning control with electronic sensor.
- Cool wall.
- Touch control frozen bread, manual ejection override and reheat settings.
- "Hi-Rise" facility lifts toast clear of slot.
- Twin hinged crumb tray.
- Cord storage.
Cat. No. 421/5293
£33.25

KENWOOD 4 SLICE TOASTER.
- Variable width bread slots.
- Variable browning control with electronic sensor.
- Cool wall.
- Frozen bread setting.
- Mid-cycle cancel button and reheat button.
- Integral bun/croissant warming rack.
- "Hi-Rise" facility lifts toast clear of slot.
- Safety jam proof switch off.
- Slide out crumb tray.
- Cord storage.
Cat. No. 421/5530
£39.00
21 £39⁰⁰

297

Use the information given on sheet 4.2 to answer these questions:

1 How many different toasters are shown?

2 How many different manufacturers make the toasters shown?

3 What price range is shown?

            lowest   *highest*

    £   £

4 What is the difference in price between the cheapest and most expensive toaster shown?

5 Write down the catalogue numbers of:

  (a) the toaster which costs £26.75

  (b) the cheapest 'cool wall' toaster

  (c) the cheapest toaster which has a frozen bread setting

  (d) the cheapest toaster with variable width bread slots

  (e) the cheapest toaster which can do one-sided toasting

6 You have £20 to spend. Write down the catalogue number of the toaster you would buy.

7 Some of the toasters have a 'microchip' browning control.

              Yes   *No*

  (a) Is that important?

  (b) Why might it persuade people to buy the toasters with microchip controls?

8 What extra features does the most expensive toaster have which the others don't have?

9 You have £30 to spend. You want to buy a toaster which has the most features at that price and which offers the best value for money. Which one would you buy? Explain why you made your choice.

Using a telephone directory

A telephone directory (called *the phone book* by BT) is a useful source of information because it can put you in touch with other people, organisations and businesses. Like a dictionary and an encyclopedia, it is arranged in **alphabetical order** by people's surnames and the names of shops, businesses and so on.

Each phone book has a contents page which tells you where to look for general information and consumer advice. In the main alphabetical section of the phone book, you will find emergency and information numbers for gas companies in a display box under the letter **G**.

Under which letters of the alphabet would you exect to find display boxes listing numbers for these services?

1 Police ☐

2 Benefits Agency ☐

3 Electricity ☐

4 Water ☐

5 Contributions Agency ☐

6 Health Service ☐

Local councils and other big organisations usually have a display box in the phone box under their own name. Under which letter of the alphabet would you look for display boxes giving contact numbers for these councils and organisations?

7 Derby City Council ☐

8 Lambeth Borough Council ☐

9 Aylesbury Vale District Council ☐

10 Gloucestershire County Council ☐

11 Halifax Building Society ☐

12 RSPCA ☐

The phone book's contents page will tell you where to find the *Useful Numbers* pages, which give the telephone numbers for lots of local organisations or services which can help you. Look at this Useful Numbers section from one edition of the phone book:

HELP AND SUPPORT

AIDS
    Personal Advice 0800 567123
    General Information 0800 555777
Alcoholics Anonymous .... **Oxford (01865) 242373**
Al-Anon for Relatives 0171 403 0888
Bucks Council on Alcohol &
    Drugs ....**Aylesbury (01296) 25329**
Childline - for children in danger or trouble -
    speak to someone who cares 0800 1111
NSPCC Child Protection Helpline
    Advice & Referrals
    24 Hour Service 0800 800500
QUIT-
    Helping smokers to quit 0171 487 3000
Samaritans
    Amersham ....**Amersham (01494) 432000**
    Banbury .... **Banbury (01295) 270000**
    Oxford .... **Oxford (01865) 722122**
Saneline
    (Support and Information about
    Mental Health Problems) 0171 724 8000

POLICE

Thames Valley
    Headquarters .... Kidlington **(01865) 846000**
    Aylesbury .... Aylesbury **(01296) 396000**

TIME

Speaking Clock 123

TRAVEL

AIR
Gatwick Airport - Please contact the
    appropriate Airline direct
Heathrow London Airport 0181 759 4321
London Luton Airport .... **Luton (01582) 405100**
Stansted Airport .... (01279) 680500
Birmingham Airport 0121 767 5511
Manchester Airport 0161 489 3000

BUS & COACH
National Express Oxford .... (01865) 791579
Oxford Bus Company (Timetable
    Information) .... **Oxford (01865) 711312**

RAIL
Aylesbury .... **High Wycombe (01494) 441561**
Chiltern Travelcheck 0171 333 3179
London, Marylebone 0171 928 5100

MOTORING
AA - 24 Hour Breakdown 0800 887766
RAC Motoring Services
    - 24 Hour Breakdown 0800 828282

13 0800 numbers are free. Write down the 0800 number you would call if:

(*a*) your car has broken down [   ] or [   ]

(*b*) you are concerned about the way your neighbours
    are treating their baby and want the NSPCC to investigate [   ]

(*c*) you need to call Childline [   ]

14 Which telephone service do you get if you just dial 123? [   ]

15 (*a*) If you live near Aylesbury and want to alert the police
    to someone acting suspiciously, which number would
    you call? [   ]

(*b*) But if the situation looked urgent or dangerous, which
    number should you dial *immediately*? [   ]

16 You want your parents to kick the smoking habit. [   ]
Which number can help them?

Look at this extract from the main alphabetical section of a telephone directory:

Madden D, 14 School La, Harton	Manfield 671035
Marsden Roy, Hobson Cottage, Trenedar	Stanford 872403
Martin Auto Repairs, High St, Ifield	Ifield 541306
Martin J.H, 44 The Leys, Harton	Manfield 671187
Masefield W, 10 Stanmore La, Lawton	Chapelton 390899
Maslen T.R, 9 Cedar Rd, Bassett	Manfield 671930
Mason C, 4 Addingrove, Lawton	Chapelton 390463
Master Class Instruments Ltd, Mill Sq, Bassett	Manfield 671344
Matthews L.F, 5B The Close, Hanley	Hanley 450176
Maughan John, Rose Cottage, Chapelton	Chapelton 390506
Maxwell V, 31 Church Sq, Harton	Manfield 671298
Mayer B, 18 Hill Close, Ifield	Ifield 541650
Maynard & Thursby (Solrs.), 24 Main Rd, Hanley	Hanley 450133
Mead A.W, 66 Back St, Bassett	Manfield 671884
Mead Carpets Ltd, 14-16 Main Rd, Hanley	Hanley 450591
Meade Dr J, The Surgery, Ifield	Ifield 541228
Meadows D.H, 39 Station Rd, Hanley	Hanley 450430
Meals on Wheels, Ivy Cottage, High St, Lawton	Chapelton 390521
Mellor R.S, Old School House, Trenedar	Stanford 872447
Mercers Stores, 7 Avenue Rise, Bassett	Manfield 671005
Merrett D, 20 The Leys, Harton	Manfield 671225
Merton S.N, 53 Cooks La, Hanley	Hanley 450411

Answer these questions:

17 Which surnames occur more than once?

18 Skim the list as quickly as you can to find the telephone numbers of:

(a) John Maughan

(b) A.W. Mead

(c) Roy Marsden

(d) Mercers Stores

(e) C. Mason

(f) Meals on Wheels

19 Who has these telephone numbers?

(a) Manfield 671225

(b) Stanford 872403

(c) Chapelton 390463

(d) Manfield 671035

20 Which two people live in the same street?

21 Write down the names of the businesses listed

22 Write down the telephone number you would ring if you wanted to:

(a) buy a violin

(b) have your car repaired

(c) buy some food

23 Write down these names as they would be listed in a telephone directory:

(a) M.L. Brady

(b) Ann Evans

(c) Dr C. Davis

(d) The Coach and Horses

24 If these people were also listed in the part of the directory shown on sheet 5.3, which name would they come **after**?

(a) Mentor Computer Systems plc

(b) Meatpak (Wholesalers) Ltd

(c) Geoffrey Maitland

25 Use your local telephone directory to write down the telephone numbers of the people listed below.

If there is more than one person with the same name and initials, write down the number of the **first** one listed.

(a) Carol Brown

(b) Michael A. Jones

(c) Paul Smith

(d) Asif Kumar

(e) Sheila Baker

(f) Lennon Williams

(g) Eleanor Price

(h) British Rail (Passenger Train Information)

(i) Tariq Malik

(j) Chris Johnson

This is another directory produced by BT (British Telecom). It is a very large list of businesses, public services and organisations, arranged in alphabetical order by **subjects**. To find the subject you want, you need to look in the **index** at the back of *Yellow Pages*. Here is part of the index from one edition of *Yellow Pages*:

MOBILE TOILETS	
See: Toilets—portable	892
MODEL AEROPLANES	
See: Model mfrs—toys & hobbies	594
Model shops	594
MODEL AGENCIES	594
MODEL MFRS—TOYS & HOBBIES	594
See also: Toy & game mfrs & importers	898
MODEL SHOPS	594
See also: Toy & game shops	899
MODELS—ARCHITECTURAL & ENGINEERING	594
MONEY LENDERS	
See: Credit & finance companies	267
Pawnbrokers	662
MONUMENTAL MASONS	595
See also: Funeral directors	420
Stonemasons & drystone wallers	857
MORTAR MFRS	596
MORTGAGE BROKERS	596
See also: Banks & financial institutions	49
Building societies	98
Financial advisers	392
Insurance brokers	528
Life assurance & pension consultants	564
MOSAIC, TERRAZZO & GRANOLITHIC FLOORING	
See: Flooring services	403
Paving services	659
Tile mfrs & suppliers	886
Tilers	888
MOSQUES	
See: Places of worship	689
MOT TESTING	598
See also: Garage services	434
MOTELS	
See: Hotels & inns	494
MOTOR BOATS & CRUISERS	
See: Boat hire	71
MOTOR CARAVANS	600
See also: Car & coach body builders	132
Car dealers & distributors	137
Caravan agents & dealers	166
Caravan hire	167
Caravan mfrs	167
Caravan repairs & service	167
MOTOR CYCLE ACCESSORIES	601
See also: Motor cycle part wh'salers	601
MOTOR CYCLE BREAKDOWN RECOVERY	601
MOTOR CYCLE ENGINEERS	601
See also: Motor cycle & scooter dealers	601

MUSIC	
See: Hi-fi dealers	491
Music arrangers & composers	606
Music publishing	606
Music schools	606
Music studios & practice rooms	606
Music teachers	606
Musical instrument & music shops	606
Musical instrument tuning & repair	608
Musicians	608
Organ dealers	640
Piano mfrs & dealers	684
Piano tuning & repair	685
MUSIC ARRANGERS & COMPOSERS	606
MUSIC MANAGEMENT & PROMOTION	606
See also: Record companies	742
MUSIC PUBLISHING	606
MUSIC SCHOOLS	606
See also: Music teachers	606
MUSIC SHOPS	
See: Musical instrument & music shops	606
MUSIC STUDIOS & PRACTICE ROOMS	606
MUSIC SYSTEMS—COMMERCIAL	
See: Sound eqpt installations	845
Sound eqpt systems	846
MUSIC TEACHERS	606
See also: Music schools	606
Tutoring	912
MUSICAL INSTRUMENT ACCESSORIES	606
MUSICAL INSTRUMENT MFRS & WH'SALERS	606
MUSICAL INSTRUMENT & MUSIC SHOPS	606
See also: Organ dealers	640
Piano mfrs & dealers	684
MUSICAL INSTRUMENT TUNING & REPAIR	608
See also: Organ builders	640
Organ dealers	640
Piano tuning & repair	685
MUSICIANS	608
See also: Entertainers	364

N 🄰 *find it fast*

NAME PLATES	608
NANNIES	
See: Domestic services	301
Employment agencies & consultants	354

Use the index section to answer these questions:

1 On which pages will you find businesses or organisations involved in the following activities?

(a) model shops ▢

(b) motels ▢

(c) musicians ▢

(d) mortgage brokers ▢

(e) name plates ▢

2 What will you find on these pages?

(a) 98 ▢

(b) 899 ▢

(c) 71 ▢

(d) 640 ▢

(e) 301 ▢

3 What main subject-heading would you give for the activities on page 606?

The index of *Yellow Pages* will often point you in the right direction, even if you can't find the subject you are looking for. So you won't find a section in *Yellow Pages* called 'Motor Boats' - you will find them listed under **Boat Hire** on page 71.

4 What subject-headings will you find these listed under?

(*a*) motels

(*b*) mosques

(*c*) mobile toilets

The index also points you to other cross-references (other subjects connected with the main one you are looking for). So you'll find businesses which do **MOT testing** of vehicles on page 598, but the index also points you to **Garage Services** on page 434.

5 Which other subjects and pages does the index point you to if you are looking for:

	Subject	Page
(*a*) musicians?		
(*b*) model shops?		
(*c*) music schools?		

Use the index of your local edition of *Yellow Pages* to write down the subjects you will find these listed under:

6 frozen food

7 gliding lessons

8 surfing equipment

9 domestic appliances

10 paper cups

Let's look at what's on page 606 of this edition of *Yellow Pages*:

---

606 MUSIC

MUSICAL INSTRUMENT

Music

See:
- Hi-Fi Dealers
- Music Arrangers & Composers
- Music Publishing
- Music Schools
- Music Studios & Practice Rooms
- Music Teachers
- Musical Instrument & Music Shops
- Musical Instrument Tuning & Repair
- Musicians
- Organ Dealers
- Piano Mfrs & Dealers
- Piano Tuning & Repair

Music arrangers & composers

Electrotrax, 44 Cropwell Bishop, Emerson Valley............**Milton Keynes 502537**
Portlock Nicholas, Hall Farm,Turvey.......**Turvey(Beds) 881777**

Music management & promotion

See Also:
- Record Companies

Resist, 173 Granby Court,Bletchley..........**Milton Keynes 371194**

RESIST PROMOTIONS

Specialists In Dance Music & Club Events   **(01908) 371194**
173 Granby Court, Granby, Bletchley

Music publishing

Poco Ltd, 29 Willian Way...........**Letchworth 671337**
Ridgmont Publishing, The Old Forge Station Rd.......**Ridgmont 280767**

Music schools

See Also:
- Music Teachers

New School Of Organ Studies The, 14 Alton Rd.......**Luton 481216**
North Buckinghamshire Music Centre, The Pavillion Sherwood Drive,Bletchley....**Milton Keynes 373786**
north Herts Music School, Highbury Rd......**Hitchin 434052**
Stables The, Wavendon......**Milton Keynes 583928**
          Milton Keynes 582522
Yamaha Music School, 263 Queensway,Bletchley......**Milton Keynes 370285**

Lewinski M, 7 Stuart Rd,Barton-le-Clay............**Luton 882703**

LORRAINE M.A. FORSDICK GTCL FTCL L. MUSTCL LTCL

Piano/Keyboard/Theory-Any Level
3.Wendover Way Luton. (01582) 419678

NOEL HOLBURN GGSM

PIANO TUITION-MEMBER OF I.S.M
4 Cloudberry, Walnut Tree
Milton Keynes   (01908) 609730

North Street Music, 5 North St........**Leighton Buzzd 372736**
O'Loughlin Micheal, 27 Warwick Avenue........**Bedford 344494**
Wesley N.J, 127 Farley Hill.......**Luton 29676**

Musical instrument accessories

Gordge M.A, 3 Mount Avenue,Bletchley........**Milton Keynes 647186**
Le Blond W.E, 206 High St Nth........**Dunstable 609310**

Musical instrument mfrs & wh'salers

Blue Mountain Systems, Nelson House,Potterspury.......**Yardley Gobion 542336**
Patrick Eggle Guitars, Unit 8 Enterprise Park,Claggy Rd,Kimptonr....**Kimpton 833133**
Pearl (U.K) Ltd, Sherbourne Drive,Tilbrook.......**Milton Keynes 366941**
          Milton Keynes 640563
Roser Amplification, 89 Eldon Rd........**Luton 494252**
Sound Technology plc, 17 Letchworth Point Dunhams Lane....**Letchworth 480000**
Washburn (UK) Ltd, 15 Amor Way,Letchworth Point.......**Letchworth 482466**
Yamaha-Kemble Music (UK) Ltd, Sherbourne Drive,Tilbrook......**Milton Keynes 366700**

Musical instrument & music shops

See Also:
- Organ Dealers
- Piano Mfrs & Dealers

ALEC LEADER KEYBOARDS

(01279) 725876
1 Duckling Lane,The Square,
Sawbridgeworth,Herts CM21 9QA

Arndale Music Ltd, 1 The Luton Arndale Centre........**Luton 484070**
Benslow Music Trust, Ibberson Way........**Hitchin 420748**
Book Castle The, 12 Church St.......**Dunstable 605670**

BEECHER ACOUSTICS OXFORD
for instruments of the violin family
- Repair & restoration
- Sales – Instruments (all sizes), bows & all accessories
- Assessment & tone improvement
- Insurance valuations
- Instruments purchased

The Old Bakery
1 Quarry High Street
Headington, Oxford OX3 8JT
tel. (01865) 62287

DAVID SNELLING VIOLINS

VIOLINS, VIOLAS, CELLOS ETC

REPAIRS & RESTORATIONS
Instruments Purchased-Valuations
KIBWORTH (0533) 793212
9 Station St, Kibworth Beauchamp,
Leicester LE8 0LN

Direction Europe Ltd, 140 High St,Cranfield........**Bedford 750515**
DRUM CLINIC, 353 Whaddon Way Bletchley Milton Keynes MK3 7LR.......**(01908) 647540**

DRUM PAD, THE

YOUR ONE-STOP PERCUSSION SHOP

Specialist Advice-Repairs-Tuition
Rehearsal-Educational Supplies

14 Grove Road
Northampton   Tel (01604) 602025

Now use this information to answer these questions:

1 How many columns is the page divided into? ☐

2 How do you know where each new subject begins?

☐

3 Which logo is used at the start of each new subject-heading?

☐

---

4 (a) What are the words in capitals at

the top of page 606 called?

CLUE: REMEMBER LOOKING AT DICTIONARIES?

(b) The first subject on page 606 is

and the last subject on page 606 is

5 Which subject-headings are these listed under?

(a) Electrotrax

(b) Arndale Music Ltd

(c) W.E. Le Blond

(d) Roser Amplification

(e) The Stables

6 Which organisations have these telephone numbers?

(a) (01908) 371194

(b) (01604) 602025

(c) (01279) 725876

(d) (01865) 62287

(e) (01908) 609730

7 Write down who you would telephone if you wanted to:

(a) get a cello repaired

(b) buy a keyboard

(c) buy a drum kit

8 Write down the telephone numbers of these organisations and people:

(a) Washburn (UK) Ltd

(b) Direction Europe Ltd

(c) Nicholas Portlock

Look through your local *Yellow Pages* to answer these.

Remember to use the alphabetical index to find the subject you are looking for.

1 You want to buy a Renault car from your nearest dealer.
Write down the name and address of the showroom.

2 You need your tennis racquet re-strung.
Who would you telephone?

3 Where would you go to buy a classical guitar?

4 What is the name of your nearest Chinese restaurant?

5 Write down the address and telephone number of the chemist nearest to your house.

6 Under which subject-heading will you find the telephone number of your college or school?

7 Which company has the largest double-glazing advertisement?

8 Who could you hire a motorised caravan from?

9 Under which subject-heading will you find your doctor listed?

10 Good painters and decorators usually belong to a national organisation called a 'guild' or 'federation'. Make a list of the different organisations whose symbols are displayed in the advertisements.

Now use your local telephone directory and *Yellow Pages* to work out who to telephone if you:

11 find a gas leak

12 think your electricity bill is too high

13 want to get the pavement outside your house repaired

Most domestic ('residential') telephone lines are connected to BT (British Telecom) and you pay a bill every quarter (once every three months), based on the calls you make.

The cost of each call depends on:

- the distance you are calling
- whether you are calling a UK number or a number in another country
- whether you are calling an information or entertainment service
- whether you are calling a mobile phone number

Look at these tables of call charges:

Guide to the cost of local and national calls.

These tables show you approximately how much a 3 minute and a 5 minute direct dialled call costs. As you may know, BT charges for calls in whole units; we also show you the time allowed for each unit.

The examples below have been calculated using the basic unit rate of 4.935p including VAT. The unit rate will be lower if you use enough units under standard call charges or if you are on Option 15.

Remember that any call to a **Free**fone 0800 number is free. Calls to **Lo**-call 0345 numbers are charged at local rates. And Freefone name calls are also free – just ring the Operator on 100 and ask for the Freefone name you want.

Local calls (notes 2-4) (L)

Seconds per unit	3 mins	5 mins
220.00	5p	10p
80.00	15p	20p

TIMINGS OF CHARGE RATE
Cheap: Mon to Fri 6pm-8am. All weekend
Daytime: Mon to Fri 8am-6pm

National 'a' rate calls (notes 2-4)
National Calls up to 56.4km (approx 35 miles) between charge points outside local call area.

Seconds per unit	3 mins	5 mins
90.00	10p	20p
80.80	15p	20p
36.15	25p	45p

National 'b1' rate calls (notes 2-4)
National Calls over 56.4km (approx 35 miles) between charge points, connected over low cost routes.

90.00	10p	20p
50.35	20p	30p
32.00	30p	50p

National 'b' rate calls (notes 2-4)
National Calls over 56.4km (approx 35 miles) between charge points, calls to the Channel Islands and Isle of Man.

90.00	10p	20p
37.95	25p	40p
25.60	40p	60p

TIMINGS OF CHARGE RATE
Weekend: All day Sat & Sun
Cheap: Mon to Fri 6pm-8am
Daytime: Mon to Fri 8am-6pm

Basic unit rate 4.935p including VAT
National 'a', 'b1' and 'b' weekend charge rate.
Cheap charge rate.
Daytime charge rate.

Calls to Personal Communication Network telephones (notes 2 & 4) (d)

Seconds per unit	3 mins	5 mins
35.14	30p	45p
22.56	40p	70p
16.52	55p	94p

TIMINGS OF CHARGE RATE
Cheap: Mon to Fri 6pm-8am. All weekend
Standard: Mon to Fri 8am-9am & 1pm-6pm
Peak: Mon to Fri 9am-1pm

Calls to numbers beginning 0956 and 0973 are charged at 'd' rate.

Calls to information & entertainment services (notes 2 & 4) (p1)
Charges effective 31/3/94

Seconds per unit	3 mins	5 mins
7.60	£1.19	£1.98
6.10	£1.49	£2.47
6.10	£1.49	£2.47

TIMINGS OF CHARGE RATE
Cheap: Mon to Fri 6pm-8am. All weekend
Standard: Mon to Fri 8am-9am & 1pm-6pm
Peak: Mon to Fri 9am-1pm

Numbers beginning 0336, 0338, 0660, 08364, 0839, 0891 and 0898 are charged at 'p1' rate. Free call barring available to customers on digital exchanges – just call us free on 150.

Calls to mobile telephones (m) (notes 2 & 4)

Seconds per unit	3 mins	5 mins
11.40	79p	£1.34
7.61	£1.19	£1.98
7.61	£1.19	£1.98

TIMINGS OF CHARGE RATE
Cheap: Mon to Fri 6pm-8am. All weekend
Standard: Mon to Fri 8am-9am & 1pm-6pm
Peak: Mon to Fri 9am-1pm

Numbers beginning 0860, 0850, 0831, 0836, 0370, 0374, 0385 and 0881 are charged at 'm' rate.

Calls to some numbers beginning 0836, 03745 and 03856 are charged at a lower rate. Calls to 08364 are charged at 'p1' rate.

Calls will also be chargeable when they are answered by mobile networks by means of a recorded announcement on the called number's behalf.

Basic unit rate 4.935p including VAT
Cheap charge rate.
Standard charge rate.
Peak charge rate.

(1995 rates)

Use the information on the tables to answer these questions:

1 On which days and between which times are:

(a) Local calls charged at the Daytime charge rate?

(b) National calls charged at the Daytime charge rate?

(c) National calls charged at the Cheap charge rate?

(d) National calls charged at the Weekend charge rate?

(e) Calls to mobile phones charged at the Peak charge rate?

2 Apart from local calls, which three types of national call distance are there? (Each type is identified by a letter):

_____ rate calls   _____ rate calls   and   _____ rate calls

3 What are the three charge rate time bands for local and national calls?

_____ charge rate

_____ charge rate

_____ charge rate

4 There are three charge rate bands for calls to information and entertainment services and to mobile phones:

_____ charge rate

_____ charge rate

_____ charge rate

Each table shows you how much time you get for each basic unit of cost (4.935p). You get more call time for each unit of 4.935p on a local call than for a national call or a call to a mobile phone.

5 How much time (in seconds) do you get for each unit on:

(a) a Local call at Daytime rate?

(b) a National 'a' rate call at Weekend rate?

(c) a National 'b1' rate call at Cheap rate?

(d) a National 'b' rate call at Daytime rate?

(e) a call to a mobile phone at Standard rate?

6 The most expensive calls will have the [   ] number of seconds for each unit.

7 Tick the most expensive call: ✔

   (a) a National 'b' rate call at Daytime rate   [   ]

   (b) a call to an information service at Cheap rate [   ]

   (c) a call to a mobile phone at Peak rate   [   ]

8 How many hours each day are charged at:

   (a) Daytime rate? [   ]   (c) Peak rate?   [   ]

   (b) Weekend rate? [   ]   (d) Standard rate? [   ]

9 On which days of the week are calls charged at only one rate?

   [   ]

10 Work out the cost of these calls:

   (a) a 3-minute call to a local number
       at 10.00 am on Monday
       [   ]

   (b) a 5-minute call to a number over
       56.4 km (not a low cost route) at
       7.30 pm on Friday
       [   ]

   (c) a 6-minute call to a mobile phone
       at 11.00 am on Saturday
       [   ]

   (d) a 3-minute call to an entertainment
       service at 5.00 pm on Wednesday
       [   ]

   (e) a 10-minute call to a number less
       than 56.4 km at 3.00 pm on Tuesday
       [   ]

Each town in the UK has its own dialling code. To dial someone in another town, you dial the dialling code first, then the telephone number. A list of towns and dialling codes is found in the front of the telephone directory.

Here is part of the list of dialling codes:

Highclere	01635	Hook (*Hants*)	01256
Highcliffe	01425	Hook Norton	01608
High Ercall	01952	Hopeman	01343
High Halden	01233	Hope Valley	01433
Highley	01746	Horam Road	01435
High Wycombe	01494	Horley	01293
Hildenborough	01732	Hornby	0152 42
Hilderstone	01889	Horncastle	01507
Hillington	01485	Hornchurch	01708
Hillsborough	01846	Horndean	01705
Hillside	01674	Horning	01692
Hillswick		Horns Cross	01237
(*3 fig. nos.*)	0180 623	Hornsea	01964
(*6 fig. nos.*)	01806	Horringer	01284
Hilmarton	01249	Horsham (*West Sussex*)	01403
Himbleton		Horsington	01526
(*3 fig. nos.*)	0190 569	Horton-in-Ribblesdale	01729
(*6 fig. nos.*)	01905	Horwich (*Lancs*)	01204
Hinckley	01455	Hovingham	01653
Hindhead (*Surrey*)	01428	How Caple	
Hindon	01747	(*3 fig. nos.*)	0198 986
Hintlesham	01473	(*6 fig. nos.*)	01989
Hirwaun	01685	Howden	01430
Hitchin	01462	Hoxne	01379
Hoar Cross		Hoy	
(*3 fig. nos.*)	0128 375	(*3 fig. nos.*)	0185 679
(*6 fig. nos.*)	01283	(*6 fig. nos.*)	01856
Hoddesdon	01992	Hubberts Bridge	01205
Hodnet	01630	Huddersfield	01484
Hoghton	01254	Hull	01482
Holbeach	01406	Humbie	01875
Holbeach St. John	01406	Hundon (*Suffolk*)	01440

Use the information on the dialling codes list to answer these questions:

1   How are the towns listed?

2   Write down the dialling codes for these places:

(*a*)   Hovingham

(*b*)   Highley

(*c*)   Hull

(*d*)   Hinckley

(*e*)   Hope Valley

3 Which towns have these dialling codes?

(a) 01747

(b) 01205

(c) 01608

(d) 01494

(e) 01964

4 If these towns were added to the list, which town would they come **after**?

(a) Hoadington

(b) Hillcrest

(c) Hothorpe

(d) Hintleborough

(e) Howthorpe

Also at the front of the telephone directory is a list of towns charged at *Local* or *National* ('a' or 'b') rates. Here is part of one charge list:

■ *LOCAL CALL AREA*
Calls to the following exchanges are charged at 'L' rate.

Aldbury Common
Amersham
Ampthill
Aylesbury
Beaconsfield

Great Missenden
Grendon Underwood
Haddenham
Harpenden
Heath and Reach
Hemel Hempstead
High Wycombe
Ickford
Kingston Blount
Leighton Buzzard
Lillingstone Dayrell

■ *CALLS UP TO 35 MILES*
Calls to exchanges listed below are charged at 'a' rate.

Abingdon
Arborfield Cross
Ascot
Ashford *(Middlesex)*
Ashwell
Asthall Leigh
Bagshot
Baldock
Bampton Castle

Gerrards Cross
Goring-on-Thames
Great Gransden
Harefield
Hatfield *(Herts)*
Haynes *(Beds)*
Heckfield
Henley-on-Thames
Hertford
Hitchin
Hoddesdon
Iver
Kidlington
Kidmore end

■ *CALLS OVER 35 MILES*
other calls are charged at 'b' rate.

5 Use the information on the list to write the charge rate letter for these towns in the boxes:

L (Local)   **a** (National rate 'a')   **b** (National rate 'b')

(a) Hitchin

(b) Horncastle

(c) Hindhead

(d) Hook Norton

(e) High Wycombe

The bad news about making telephone calls is that you have to pay for them! BT send you a telephone bill every **quarter** (every three months), which tells you how much you have to pay. The telephone bill contains the following information:

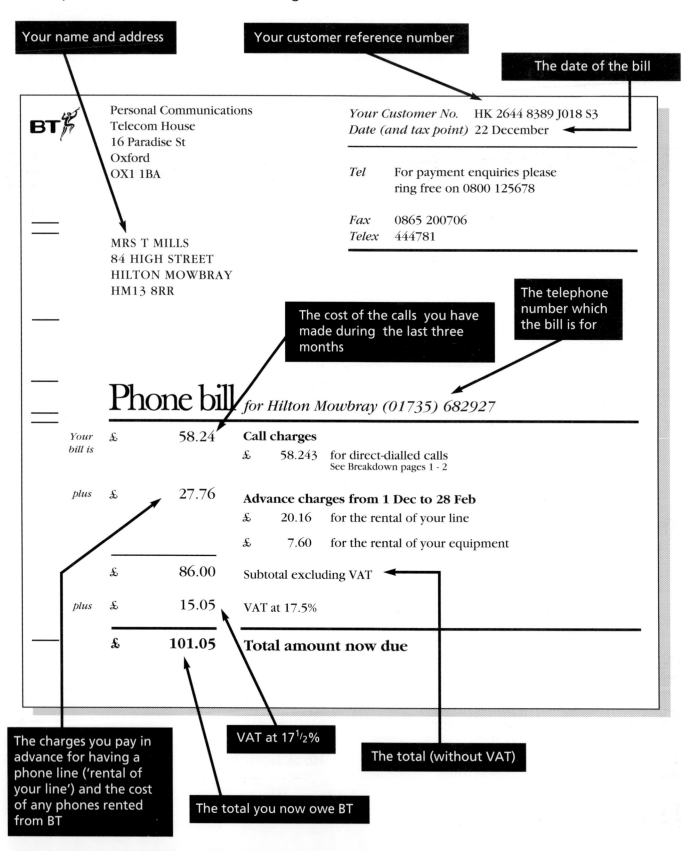

Your name and address

Your customer reference number

The date of the bill

BT

Personal Communications
Telecom House
16 Paradise St
Oxford
OX1 1BA

Your Customer No. HK 2644 8389 J018 S3
Date (and tax point) 22 December

Tel   For payment enquiries please
        ring free on 0800 125678

Fax   0865 200706
Telex   444781

MRS T MILLS
84 HIGH STREET
HILTON MOWBRAY
HM13 8RR

The cost of the calls you have made during the last three months

The telephone number which the bill is for

Phone bill *for Hilton Mowbray (01735) 682927*

Your bill is	£	58.24	**Call charges**
			£ 58.243 for direct-dialled calls
			See Breakdown pages 1 - 2
plus	£	27.76	**Advance charges from 1 Dec to 28 Feb**
			£ 20.16 for the rental of your line
			£ 7.60 for the rental of your equipment
	£	86.00	Subtotal excluding VAT
plus	£	15.05	VAT at 17.5%
	£	**101.05**	**Total amount now due**

The charges you pay in advance for having a phone line ('rental of your line') and the cost of any phones rented from BT

VAT at 17½%

The total (without VAT)

The total you now owe BT

Your phone bill will not itemise calls which last less than 10 units (42p). It just shows the total of these short calls, like this:

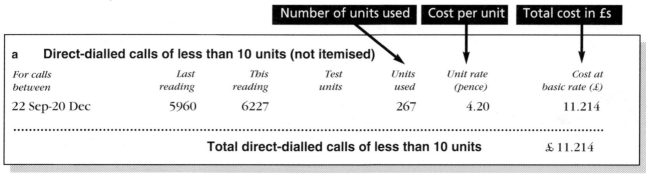

| | Number of units used | Cost per unit | Total cost in £s |

a   Direct-dialled calls of less than 10 units (not itemised)

For calls between	Last reading	This reading	Test units	Units used	Unit rate (pence)	Cost at basic rate (£)
22 Sep-20 Dec	5960	6227		267	4.20	11.214

Total direct-dialled calls of less than 10 units		**£ 11.214**

Any calls of 10 units or over are then itemised, so you can see:

| When a call was made | What time the call was made | The telephone number dialled | The length of the call | The number of units | The cost of the call |

Date	Time	Destination		Duration (mins:secs)	Units used	Cost at basic rate(£)
26 Sep	15:54	Aylesbury	01296 8382000	20:01	16	0.672
2 Oct	12:50	Milton Keynes	01908 7364255	16:48	13	0.546
6 Oct	19.04	High Wycombe	01494 2301952	33:18	10	0.42
14 Oct	21:20	Chesham	01494 7276044	67:44	19	0.798
20 Oct	16:29	London	0171 5902362	9:04	16	0.672
25 Oct	09:52	Premium rate	0891 6422870	1:04	11	0.462
29 Oct	10:05	Burford	01993 2551177	72:06	20	0.84
3 Nov	21:48	Horsham	01403 5008232	24:00	29	1.218
13 Nov	12:13	Glasgow	0141 9824909	18:47	13	0.546
28 Nov	22:25	Reading	01734 2316520	54:31	41	1.722
10 Dec	08:54	London	0181 6748049	13:18	12	0.504
20 Dec	11.24	Glasgow	0141 9824909	23:01	16	0.672

1 Complete the bill totals:

	Units	Cost
Total direct-dialled calls of 10 units and over		£

2 Which telephone number is this bill for?

3 What is the customer number?

4 What is the date of the bill?

5 What is the total telephone bill?   £

6 How many calls over 10 units were made in:

(a) October? ☐ (b) November? ☐ (c) December? ☐

7 On which date was:

(a) the longest call made?

(b) the most expensive call made?

(c) the earliest call made?

(d) the latest call made?

8 Which destination used the most units?

9 Why didn't the longest call use as many units?

10 Tick these if they affect the cost of your telephone calls:

	✔	Why?
(a) The day of the week on which you make your call	☐	
(b) The time of day you make your call	☐	
(c) Whether you phone a house or a business	☐	
(d) Whether you phone an ordinary phone or a mobile phone	☐	
(e) Whether you talk to more than one person when you call	☐	
(f) How long your call lasts	☐	
(g) How far away the call destination is	☐	
(h) Whether your call is a national or international call	☐	

You can work out how much it costs to phone people in other countries by using the information provided by BT in these charge tables:

Calling abroad? Here's how much it will cost.

These tables show you approximately how much a 5 minute and a 10 minute international direct dialled call costs. We also show you the time allowed for each unit.

The examples have been calculated using the basic unit rate of 4.2p (4.935p including VAT) and rounded up to the nearest whole penny. The unit rate will be lower if you use enough units under standard call charges or if you are on Option 15.

Republic of Ireland (IR) (notes 2, 4 & 11)

Seconds per unit	5 mins £	10 mins £
10.80	1.39	2.77
8.34	1.78	3.56

Timings of charge rate
Cheap: Mon-Fri 6pm-8am
All weekend
Standard:
Mon-Fri 8am-6pm

Republic of Ireland

Charge Band 1 (notes 2 & 4)

Seconds per unit	5 mins £	10 mins £
10.00	1.49	2.97
8.34	1.78	3.56

Timings of charge rate
Cheap: Mon-Fri 8pm-8am
All weekend
Standard:
Mon-Fri 8am-8pm

Andorra
Azores
Belgium
Canary Is.
Denmark
Faroe Is.
France
Germany
Gibraltar
Greece
Italy (inc.
Vatican City)
Liechtenstein
Luxembourg
Madeira
Monaco
Netherlands
Portugal
San Marino
Spain (inc.
Balearic Is.)
Switzerland

Charge Band 2 (notes 2 & 4)

Seconds per unit	5 mins £	10 mins £
6.87	2.18	4.35
5.82	2.57	5.14

Timings of charge rate
Cheap: Mon-Fri 8pm-8am
All weekend
Standard:
Mon-Fri 8am-8pm

Austria
Cyprus
Czech Republic
Finland
Hungary
Malta
Norway
Poland
Slovak Republic
Sweden

Charge Band 3 (notes 2 & 4)

Seconds per unit	5 mins £	10 mins £
5.21	2.87	5.73
4.40	3.41	6.77

Timings of charge rate
Cheap: Mon-Fri 8pm-8am
All weekend
Standard:
Mon-Fri 8am-8pm

Albania
Algeria
Bosnia-
Hercegovina
Bulgaria
Croatia
Cyprus
010 905 numbers
Iceland
Libya
Morocco
Slovenia
Tunisia
Turkey
Yugoslavia

Charge Band 4 (notes 2 & 4)

Seconds per unit	5 mins £	10 mins £
6.35	2.37	4.69
5.90	2.52	5.04

Timings of charge rate
Cheap: Mon-Fri 8pm-8am
All weekend
Standard:
Mon-Fri 8am-8pm

Canada   USA

Charge Band 5 (notes 2 & 4)

Seconds per unit	5 mins £	10 mins £
4.50	3.31	6.62
3.80	3.90	7.80

Timings of charge rate
Cheap: Mon-Fri 8pm-8am
All weekend
Standard:
Mon-Fri 8am-8pm

Anguilla
Antigua &
Barbuda
Bahamas
Barbados
Bermuda
Cayman Is.
Dominica
Dominican Rep.
Grenada (inc.
Carriacou)
Jamaica
Montserrat
Puerto Rico
St Kitts & Nevis
St Lucia
St Pierre &
Miquelon
St Vincent & The
Grenadines
Trinidad &
Tobago
Turks &
Caicos Is.
Virgin Is. (UK)
Virgin Is. (US)

Charge Band 6 (notes 2 & 4)
Charges effective 2 February 1994

Seconds per unit	5 mins £	10 mins £
5.09	2.92	5.83
4.35	3.41	6.82

Timings of charge rate
Cheap: Daily Midnight-7am
& 2.30pm-7.30pm
Standard: Daily 7am-2.30pm
& 7.30pm-Midnight

Australia   Chatham Is.   New Zealand

Charge Band 7 (notes 2 & 4)

Seconds per unit	5 mins £	10 mins £
4.06	3.66	7.31
3.26	4.59	9.13

Timings of charge rate
Cheap: Daily 8pm-8am
Standard:
Daily 8am-8pm

Singapore

Basic unit rate 4.935p including VAT
Cheap charge rate
Standard charge rate

7

(1995 rates)

---

1 These tables show ⬚ charge bands.

The first charge band is for calls to ⬚ .

2 Charge Band 4 is for calls to ⬚ and

⬚ .

3 Charge Band 7 is for calls to ⬚ .

---

4 In which Charge Bands are calls to these countries?

(*a*) Barbados 　　　　

(*d*) Spain 　　　　

(*b*) Malta

(*e*) Croatia

(*c*) New Zealand

5 There are two charge rates (Cheap and Standard) for international calls. Which charge rate would these calls be charged at?

(*a*) USA at 6.00 pm on Friday

(*b*) Australia at 10.00 pm on Monday

(*c*) Czech Republic at 9.00 pm on Wednesday

(*d*) Jamaica at 11.00 am on Sunday

(*e*) Republic of Ireland at 6.30 pm on Thursday

6 Each metered call unit costs 4.2p plus VAT. How many seconds would you get for each unit on these calls?

(*a*) Poland at 9.00 am on Monday

(*b*) Trinidad at 7.30 am on Tuesday

(*c*) Portugal at 11.30 pm on Saturday

(*d*) Turkey at 2.00 pm on Friday

(*e*) USA at 6.00 am on Wednesday

It's your turn this week to take the sandwich order for your office.
Everyone has given you their order and the money:

CHRISTOS
1 SAUSAGE
1 BACON
1 HAM
COFFEE (LARGE)

Andy
1 cheese
1 ham
1 large tea

Tracey
bacon x2
small coffee

SANDWICHES
- cheese 80p
- ham 80p
- sausage 60p
- bacon 60p
- salad 70p
(toasted 20p extra)

Tea Large 50p Small 40p
Coffee Large 80p Small 50p

Neema
small tea
1x toasted
ham
1x cheese

Reg
two toasted
cheese
large tea

SHARDA
3 SALAD
LARGE COFFEE

1 Write out the order for the sandwich bar and add up the cost:

> 2 x cheese   £1.60
>
>
>
>
>
>
>
>   _____
>   Total

When you collect the order, you find that you've only got £13.60. Someone's given you the wrong money. You check back and find that Andy gave you £2.10, Tracey gave you £1.70, Reg gave you £2.10, Christos gave you £2.80, Neema gave you £2 and Sharda gave you £2.90.

2 Who's given you the wrong money?

3 Why do you think the mistake happened?

Ravi and Marco own a café in the town centre. Almost everyone goes there, because they like to try all the different kinds of food which are served. Here is this week's menu:

Beef curry and rice	£3.50
Vegetable curry	£3.50
Vegetable casserole	£2.75
Lasagne	£2.80
Spaghetti bolognese	£2.80
Pizza	£2.50
Chicken tandoori	£3.90
Chicken tikka	£3.90
Jacket potato	
- cheese	£1.60
- baked beans	£1.90
- cottage cheese	£1.90
Egg and chips	£1.60
Steak pie and chips	£2.20
Sausage and chips	£1.80
Beefburger and chips	£1.60
Shepherd's pie	£2.40
Roast beef, roast potatoes, 2 veg	£3.50
Sweet and sour pork, fried rice	£3.70
Sweet and sour chicken, fried rice	£3.70
Ham salad	£2.25
Cheese salad	£2.25
Egg salad	£2.25
Beans on toast	90p
Sandwiches	
- cheese	80p
- ham	80p
- sausage	60p
- bacon	60p
- salad	70p
(toasted 20p extra)	

Bread	20p
Baked beans	40p
Boiled rice	95p
Fried rice	95p
Mushrooms	50p
Tomatoes	50p
Chappati	30p
Naan bread	40p
Poppadom	20p
Onion bhaji	30p

Fruit pie and cream	80p
Ice cream	60p
Chocolate sponge and custard	80p
Chocolate fudge cake	80p

Tea	Large 50p	Small 40p
Coffee	Large 80p	Small 50p
Hot chocolate		50p
Soft drinks		60p
Orange juice		60p
Mineral water		50p

1 Fill in the missing headings on the menu.

2 You drop in to the café late morning and want a snack (not a sandwich) instead of a cooked meal. You also feel thirsty. You only have £2.50. What would you get?

	Price
Total	£

3 Our favourite foods are not always the healthiest. If you had a free choice of the menu (including a drink) in the café, what would you buy? (You can eat as much as you like!) Add up the total cost.

	Price
Total	£

What change would you get from £10?

4 If you wanted to choose a meal that was as healthy as possible (including a drink), what would you buy?

	Price
Total	£

What change would you get from £10?

5 Every now and then, you, Christos and Tracey like to get out of the office and have a cooked lunch at the café. The three of you order your main course:

I'll go for sausage and chips with beans and mushrooms. And I'll have some bread – and a large tea, please.

(Christos)

I think I'll have the vegetable curry with extra fried rice, a chappati and naan bread – and a coke, please.

(Tracey)

Let me try the lasagne, please, with a couple of poppadoms. Can I have a mineral water to go with it?

(You)

After your main course, Christos still has room for chocolate sponge and he orders another large tea. Tracey says she'll try the fruit pie. You just want a small coffee.

(a) Write out the bill for each of you:

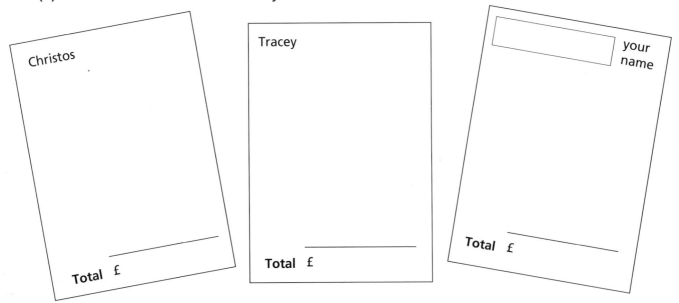

Christos

Total £

Tracey

Total £

your name

Total £

Tracey pays the bill for all three of you by giving Marco a £20 note.

(b) How much change does she get?

You and Christos give her a £5 note each for your meal.

(c) How much change does she give each of you?

You   Christos

Food shopping

You have just moved into a one-bedroom flat. You've got some furniture, a fridge/freezer and a cooker, but you haven't bought any food or cleaning items yet.

1 Make a list of the evening meals (and lunches at the weekend) that you will prepare during the week. Include desserts, if you like them!

MONDAY	TUESDAY	WEDNESDAY	THURSDAY

FRIDAY	SATURDAY	SUNDAY

2 Now make a shopping list of the items of food and drinks you will need to buy (leave the price column blank). You'll need to include other household items like cleaning materials, and don't forget to include breakfast food. You might buy some snacks, if you like them.

Shopping List

Items	Price (£)
	Total £

Here is part of the food display in the supermarket:

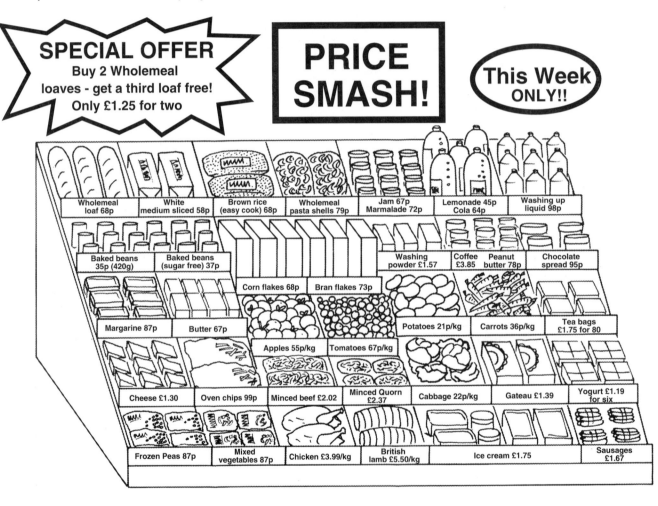

3 Look at the prices on the shelves and add them to your shopping list. Think how *many* of each item you will need. Will one loaf of bread last all week? How many tins or packets will you need to buy?

Add up the total cost of your shopping list.

The total shopping bill will be

£ [   ]

IF THE FOOD OR ITEMS YOU WANT AREN'T ON THE SHELVES, YOU CAN CHANGE THE ITEM ON YOUR SHOPPING LIST OR FIND THE PRICE AT YOUR LOCAL SUPERMARKET

Look at this trolley of shopping:

4 Compare the items in the trolley with the bill you collected at the checkout:

(a) Is the bill correct?

Yes   No

☐   ☐

(b) If 'No', what mistakes have been made?

(c) What should the total bill have been?

£

SUPERFOOD STORES PLC
14 THE PRECINCT   HOUNDSWAY
MIDDX   HL3 9TQ

Thank you for your custom

	£
BAKED BEANS 420g	0.35
BAKED BEANS 420g	0.35
SUPER COLA 1.5l	0.64
CORNFLAKES 500g	0.68
POTATOES 5 kg	1.05
ICE CREAM 5l	1.75
BROWN RICE	0.68
BROWN RICE	0.68
BROWN RICE	0.68
WASHING POWDER	1.57
YOGHURTS x6	1.19
FROZEN PEAS	0.87
FROZEN PEAS	0.87
OVEN CHIPS	0.99
WHOLEMEAL BREAD	0.68
WHOLEMEAL BREAD	0.68
WASH-UP LIQUID	0.98

BAL DUE 14.69

CASH TENDERED	20.00
CHANGE	5.31

09:45 19 JAN 99

**** PLEASE CALL AGAIN ****

A theatre seating plan is designed to help you choose the best seats for your money. Look at this theatre's seating plan and price list:

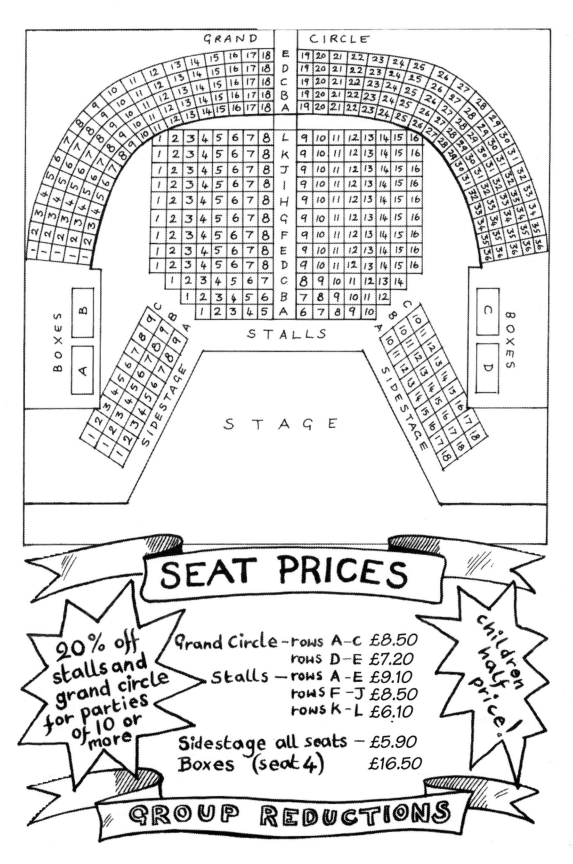

SEAT PRICES

20% off stalls and grand circle for parties of 10 or more

children half price!

Grand Circle - rows A–C £8.50
                 rows D–E £7.20
Stalls — rows A–E £9.10
        rows F–J £8.50
        rows K–L £6.10

Sidestage all seats — £5.90
Boxes (seat 4) £16.50

GROUP REDUCTIONS

Use the information on the seating plan to answer these questions:

1 Why are the first three rows of the stalls the most expensive seats?

2 Which seats are the cheapest?

Why?

3 How does it work out that the boxes are actually cheaper?

4 The seats are numbered with the row number, then the number of the seat (A1, A2 and so on).

(a) Which two seats in the stalls probably get the best view of all?

(b) Which two seats in the grand circle probably get the best view?

(c) Which two sidestage seats probably get the worse view?

(d) Which two boxes get the best view?

(e) Which two grand circle seats probably get the worse view?

5 How much would the following bookings cost?

(a) Two adults in box C.

(b) Three adults in stalls row G.

(c) Five adults in grand circle row D.

(d) Four adults in stalls seats E6, E7, F6, F7.

(e) Two adults in grand circle seats D25 and D26 and two children in the row in front.

(f) A party of twelve adults, half in stalls row K and half in sidestage row B.

(g) Mr and Mrs Landon, with their three children, in stalls row F.

6 Mike is sitting in grand circle A20 and drops his ice-cream over the balcony. Which seat does it land on?

7 Aisha and Claire are sitting in stalls J3 and J4 and notice two of their friends exactly five rows in front.

(a) What are their friends' seat numbers?

(b) How much more did their friends pay to get in?

8 Mum, Dad and their two children want to see the play on Saturday. Dad can only spare £20 for all their tickets. Unfortunately, the sidestage seats and boxes are booked. Which part of the theatre do they end up in?

9 A coach party of 35 adults and 10 children book the following seats :

Adults: Stalls rows B and C
(all seats)
Sidestage row A (9 seats)

Children: Stalls row A (all seats)

Work out the total cost of their booking.

Total cost   £ _____

10 (a) How many seats are there in the theatre? Don't count them all! Show how you worked it out.

(b) Saturday's play is a sell out. All the seats are sold to adults and there are no group reductions. Work out how much money the box-office took on Saturday. A calculator may save you time!

Getting organised

Lots of people keep a **diary** of what happens to them each day. But a diary is also very useful for planning what you have to do in future. You can make a note of birthdays, special events and holidays. You can also put meetings and other engagements in the diary, to avoid 'double booking'. Look at this double page from a 'week to view' personal organiser:

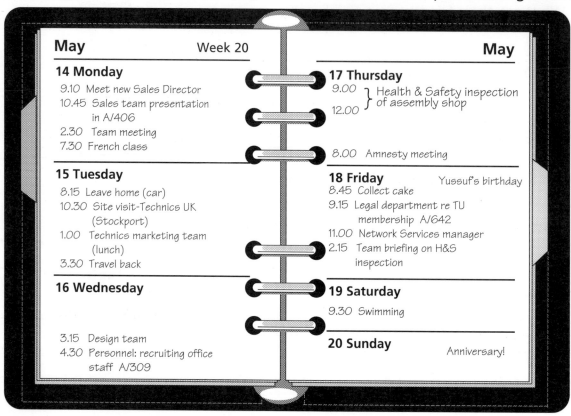

May　　　　　Week 20　　　　　　　　　　　　　　**May**

14 Monday
9.10　Meet new Sales Director
10.45　Sales team presentation
　　　　in A/406
2.30　Team meeting
7.30　French class

15 Tuesday
8.15　Leave home (car)
10.30　Site visit-Technics UK
　　　　(Stockport)
1.00　Technics marketing team
　　　　(lunch)
3.30　Travel back

16 Wednesday

3.15　Design team
4.30　Personnel: recruiting office
　　　　staff A/309

17 Thursday
9.00 ⎱ Health & Safety inspection
12.00 ⎰ of assembly shop

8.00　Amnesty meeting

18 Friday　　　　　Yussuf's birthday
8.45　Collect cake
9.15　Legal department re TU
　　　　membership A/642
11.00　Network Services manager
2.15　Team briefing on H&S
　　　　inspection

19 Saturday
9.30　Swimming

20 Sunday　　　　　Anniversary!

1　(a)　The first day shown is _____

　　(b)　The last day shown is _____

　　(c)　These two pages cover _____ days.

2　What does 'Week 20' mean? _____

3　(a)　What is the earliest time of day entered in the diary? _____

　　(b)　What is the latest time of day entered in the diary? _____

4　In which rooms do these meetings take place?

　　(a)　The meeting with Personnel _____

　　(b)　The sales team's presentation _____

　　(c)　The meeting with the Legal department _____

5 (a) Why do you think the Team Meeting is on Monday?

(b) Why is there an extra Team Meeting at the end of the week?

6 Which day is busiest?

7 How long can:

(a) the meeting with Legal Department last?

(b) the site visit to Technics UK last?

8 (a) How long does the journey to Stockport take?

(b) What time will the diary owner get home on Tuesday?

9 On which mornings or afternoons will the diary owner get a chance to catch up on paperwork?

10 (a) On which day will there be a 'working lunch'?

(b) Who is providing the lunch?

11 What spare time activities is the diary owner involved in?

12 What clue tells you that Yussuf is a member of the family or a close friend?

13 Why is Sunday 20 May a special day?

14 (a) Is the owner of the diary a man or a woman?

(b) Why do you think so? (Discuss…!)

Using the *Radio Times*

The BBC publish *Radio Times* each week as a detailed guide to television and radio programmes, including satellite TV channels. You can use *Radio Times* to help you plan the TV programmes you want to watch. After all, you can only watch one programme and record another at the same time!

On the next two sheets you will find some of the programmes shown on the network TV channels on one Wednesday evening.

Each programme entry gives you a set of basic information:

The time the programme starts

The title of the programme

12.00 The Experts
Spy comedy starring **John Travolta, Kelly Preston** Back in the days before *glasnost*, the KGB have an unusual secret weapon hidden in the heart of the Soviet Union: in an exact replica of Smalltown, USA, they are raising prospective spies as Americans. However, their conception of the States is woefully behind the times.

Travis ....JOHN TRAVOLTA
Bonnie ....KELLY PRESTON
Wendell ....ARYE GROSS
Jill ....DEBORAH FOREMAN
Yuri ....JAMES KEACH
Cameron Smith ....CHARLES MARTIN SMITH
With JAN RUBES, BRIAN DOYLE MURRAY, MIMI MAYNARD, EVE BRENT, RICK DOCOMMUN, STEVE LEVITT, TONY EDWARDS.
Director Dave Thomas (1989) *Stereo* *65155*
◆ **FILM REVIEWS pages 52-56** ◄

The programme's 'stars' (in bold type)

A summary of what the programme is about

The cast of characters

The *VideoPlus* recording code

The programme's director (and the date it was made)

Reference to other information on the programme

Look at the viewing information on sheets 18.2 and 18.3, and answer these questions:

1 What time does the first evening programme on each channel begin?

(*a*) BBC1 [   ]   (*c*) ITV [   ]

(*b*) BBC2 [   ]   (*d*) Channel 4 [   ]

2 If you switched on your TV at 6.00 pm, what choices of programme would you have?

(*a*) BBC1 [   ]   (*c*) ITV [   ]

(*b*) BBC2 [   ]   (*d*) Channel 4 [   ]

3 The [symbol] symbol is used to show films.

How many films are being shown on Wednesday evening? [   ]

WEDNESDAY 18 JANUARY

1 BBC1

5.35pm Neighbours
Helen takes a gamble for love. Gaby enjoys a flirtation. Danni and Sassy battle sexism in basketball.

Helen Daniels	ANNE HADDY
Doug Willis	TERENCE DONOVAN
Pam Willis	SUE JONES
Gaby Willis	RACHEL BLAKELY
Brad Willis	SCOTT MICHAELSON
Lou Carpenter	TOM OLIVER
Rick Alessi	DAN FALZON
Julie Martin	JULIE MULLINS
Philip Martin	IAN RAWLINGS
Hannah Martin	REBECCA RITTERS
Debbie Martin	MARNIE REECE-WILMORE
Michael Martin	TROY BECKWITH
Annalise Hartman	KIMBERLEY DAVIES
Mark Gottlieb	BRUCE SAMAZAN
Cheryl Stark	CAROLINE GILLMER
Danni Stark	ELIZA SZONERT
Brett Stark	BRETT BLEWITT
Cody Willis	PETA BRADY
Luke Foster	MURRAY BARTLETT
Sally Pritchard	BRENDA WEBB
Jesse O'Connor	JAMES RYAN
Len Mangel	JOHN LEE
Sassy	DEFAH DATTNER
Shown at 1.30pm. Stereo Subtitled 757050

6.00 Six O'Clock News
With Anna Ford and Andrew Harvey. Subtitled
Weather Suzanne Charlton 401

6.30 Regional news magazine
See Monday for details 383

7.00 This Is Your Life
Michael Aspel springs more surprises and reunions on unsuspecting guests.
Director Brian Klein; Producer Malcolm Morris
Stereo Subtitled 5418

7.30 On the Up
Tony has taken a marquee at the county show to promote his business, but some upper-class yahoos cause a big disturbance.

Tony Carpenter	DENNIS WATERMAN
Mrs Wembley	JOAN SIMS
Sam	SAM KELLY
Maggie	JENNA RUSSELL
Dawn	MICHELLE HATCH
Mrs Turner	GILLIAN WEBB
Mr Burton	PETER DENYER
Nigel	RICHARD CRIPWELL
Charles	ADAM FAHEY
Written by Bob Larbey; Director/Producer
Gareth Gwenlan Rpt Stereo Subtitled 895

8.00 How Do They Do That?
Here are some answers to questions you always wanted to ask – and a few more. All sorts of things have aroused the nation's curiosity and got us wondering – how do they do that? This week, a look at the complex organisation behind the BBC's Grandstand programme, and how two British surgeons used a unique treatment from Russia to help 1-year-old bone-disease sufferer Bethan Jones. Presented by Desmond Lynam and Jenny Hull.
Producers Martin Lucas and Gill Stribling-Wright
Executive producer Alan Boyd
Stereo Subtitled 293578
QUESTIONS: please send them to How Do They Do That?, PO Box 4653, London SE1 9UQ

8.45 Points of View
Anne Robinson with viewers' opinions on BBC television programmes. Write with your comments to Points of View, BBCtv, London W12 7RJ. Or telephone/fax on 081-576 4560. The e-mail address is: pov@bbcnc.org.uk
Producer Bernard Newnham
Stereo Subtitled 237789

9.00 Nine O'Clock News
With Michael Buerk. Subtitled
Regional News
Weather Suzanne Charlton 4383

9.30 The Private Life of Plants
CHOICE David Attenborough continues his incredible journey into the world of plants. Filming all over the world, he reveals how plants are just as exciting as animals, and often far more unusual. Growing. A look at some of the extraordinary ways in which plants gain nutrition and protection by using their leaves, spines, stings, poisons and some dramatic disappearing tricks.
See today's choices.
Executive producer Mike Salisbury
Stereo Subtitled 262692
Repeated next Monday on BBC2
◆ Guess who's coming to dinner? See page 22

10.20 Sportsnight
CHOICE Introduced by Desmond Lynam with Gary Lineker. Football Highlights of three of this evening's key FA Cup third round replays, plus goals from this evening's and last night's other matches. John Motson, Barry Davies and Clive Tyldesley provide the commentary.
Rugby Union A preview of the start of the Five Nations Championship. Wales start their defence of the title by playing France and Ireland face England.
See today's choices.
Producer Vivien Kent; Editor Brian Barwick
Stereo 576963

12.00 The Experts
Spy comedy starring John Travolta, Kelly Preston
Back in the days before glasnost, the KGB have an unusual secret weapon hidden in the heart of the Soviet Union: in an exact replica of Smalltown, USA, they are raising prospective spies as Americans. However, their conception of the States is woefully behind the times.

Travis	JOHN TRAVOLTA
Bonnie	KELLY PRESTON
Wendell	ARYE GROSS
Jill	DEBORAH FOREMAN
Yuri	JAMES KEACH
Cameron Smith	CHARLES MARTIN SMITH
With JAN RUBES, BRIAN DOYLE MURRAY, MIMI MAYNARD, EVE BRENT, RICK DOCOMMUN, STEVE LEVITT, TONY EDWARDS.
Director Dave Thomas (1989) Stereo 65155
◆ FILM REVIEWS pages 52–56

1.30-1.35am Weather

2 BBC2

5.30pm All in the Mind
Lateral thinking quiz that pits youth against experience. This week, a team of 17-year-olds from the Alun School, Mold, take on a team of bar staff. Presented by Alison Holloway.
Producers Bob Louis and Kate Marlow
Executive producer Dave Ross Stereo 760

6.00 Star Trek: the Next Generation
Starring Patrick Stewart
Disaster. When the Enterprise is powerless after a collision with a quantum filament, Jean-Luc is stuck in a lift with three children and Data loses his head. Troi is the senior officer on the bridge and holds the lives of the crew in her hands. Meanwhile Worf is forced to act as midwife to Keiko.

Captain Jean-Luc Picard	PATRICK STEWART
Commander William Riker	JONATHAN FRAKES
Lt Commander Data	BRENT SPINER
Dr Beverly Crusher	GATES MCFADDEN
Lt Commander Geordi LaForge	LEVAR BURTON
Counsellor Deanna Troi	MARINA SIRTIS
Lt Worf	MICHAEL DORN
Marissa	ERIKA FLORES
Jay Gordon	JOHN CHRISTIAN GRAAS
Keiko	ROSALIND CHAO
Stereo Subtitled 644944

6.45 Natural Born Footballers
The biggest names in the sport talk personally about the game.
This week Franz Beckenbauer, who achieved World Cup medals as both player and manager of the German national side, remembers some of his greatest moments. He discusses the transition from team player to manager, and reveals that one of the most difficult tasks of his footballing career was to mark England's Bobby Charlton during the 1966 World Cup final. Including great football action, originally seen in Standing Room Only.
Director Michael Wadding
Revised rpt Stereo 289437

7.00 The World at War
The acclaimed 26-part documentary series telling the story of the Second World War.
19: Pincers. With the liberation of Paris in August, 1944, the war is as good as over. Germany is crumbling, but it is not defeated yet. From the east the Russians advance on the Reich, successfully reclaiming the land lost in Hitler's Barbarossa operation. The Allies, meanwhile, advance from the south and west, but supply shortages and disagreement among the Allied commanders about the best method of attack hinder their progress. Montgomery and Eisenhower reach a critical point. The Americans plan to advance on a broad front while Montgomery wants a concentrated narrow attack and plans the Arnhem raid, which will end in disaster. Narrated by Laurence Olivier.
Written and directed by Peter Batty; Producer Jeremy Isaacs
First shown on ITV Subtitled 5147

8.00 Rhodes around Britain
Top chef Gary Rhodes continues his culinary voyage around the country discovering, cooking and enjoying regional produce. This week, he visits Wales where he meets Welsh rock star Mike Peters and compares the recipe for a new single and a new dish. He also discovers the delights of seafood, lamb

and Italian pecorino cheese – all made in Wales. In the kitchen he prepares mussels with garlic, almonds and parsley, and a chump of lamb marinated in red wine and orange.
Executive producer Fiona Pitcher
Rpt Stereo 2708
A BBC book Rhodes around Britain, featuring the recipes in the series, is available in hardback, price £17.99, and paperback, price £12.99.

8.30 University Challenge
In this week's second-round match of the student quiz Lampeter, Wales, take on the University of Birmingham who got through as one of the highest scoring runners-up. Both teams are battling for a place in the quarter finals. Jeremy Paxman asks the questions.
Director Jenny Dodd; Producer Kieran Roberts
Stereo Subtitled 1215

9.00 Film premiere Bridge to Silence
Drama starring Marlee Matlin Lee Remick
Injured in the car accident that claimed the life of her deaf husband, Peg Lawrence, also deaf, is unable to care for their young daughter. Peg's mother, from whom she is estranged, decides to take over, and years of resentment boil to the surface.

Peg Lawrence	MARLEE MATLIN
Marge Duffield	LEE REMICK
Al Duffield	JOSEF SOMMER
Dan Burnell	MICHAEL O'KEEFE
Lisa Lawrence	ALLISON SILVA
Mary Amblett	CANDACE BRECKER
Director Karen Arthur (1989) 3654
◆ FILM REVIEWS pages 52–56

10.30 Newsnight
With Jeremy Paxman. Subtitled ..826234

11.15 The Late Show
Tonight's edition of the music and arts magazine includes a report on new star soprano Amanda Roocroft. Presented by Fintan O'Toole. Stereo 771470

11.55 Weatherview

12.00-12.55am The Midnight Hour
A review of the political day. With Trevor Phillips.
Preceded by
The Midnight News 5196906

4.00-4.15am BBC Select
Benefits Agency Today: the magazine programme (for recording and viewing later) visits the East Midlands to look at the domestic violence service and celebrate Diwali in Leicester. 40901258

ITV CENTRAL

5.40pm Early Evening News
With John Suchet. *Subtitled*
Weather Martyn Davies 735963

6.00 Home and Away
Shown at 1.25pm *Subtitled* 842760

6.25 Regional news magazine
For details see Monday. *Subtitled* 916708

7.00 Talking Telephone Numbers
Phillip Schofield and Emma Forbes host the quiz show that gives viewers the chance to win a large cash prize. The guests this week are magician Wayne Dobson, comedian Mike Hayley and a Ukrainian acrobatic dance troupe.
Director Martin Scott; Producer Tony Nicholson
Stereo 3906

7.30 Coronation Street
CHOICE Denise registers the arrival of baby Daniel, but faces a dilemma about whether to give him Ken's surname.
See today's choices.

Mike Baldwin	JOHNNY BRIGGS
Alma Baldwin	AMANDA BARRIE
Denise Osbourne	DENISE BLACK
Ken Barlow	WILLIAM ROACHE
Sally Webster	SALLY WHITTAKER
Betty Turpin	BETTY DRIVER
Rita Sullivan	BARBARA KNOX
Des Barnes	PHILIP MIDDLEMISS
Mavis Wilton	THELMA BARLOW
Derek Wilton	PETER BALDWIN
Reg Holdsworth	KEN MORLEY
Vera Duckworth	ELIZABETH DAWN
Jim McDonald	CHARLES LAWSON
Liz McDonald	BEVERLEY CALLARD
Don Brennan	GEOFF HINSLIFF
Emily Bishop	EILEEN DERBYSHIRE
Tricia Armstrong	TRACY BRABIN
Jamie Armstrong	JOSEPH GILGUN
Maud Grimes	ELIZABETH BRADLEY
Percy Sugden	BILL WADDINGTON
Steve McDonald	SIMON GREGSON
Norris Cole	MALCOLM HEBDEN

Episode written by Martin Allen
Producer Sue Pritchard; Director Michael Kerrigan
Stereo 963

8.00 Des O'Connor Tonight
Des O'Connor hosts another show that brings together established stars and talented newcomers. This week, he is joined by film star Anthony Quinn, talented young comedian Alan Davies and Spanish actor/singer Miguel Bosé.
Director Brian Penders; Producer Colin Fay
Stereo 1321

9.00 Taggart
Prayer for the Dead (part 2). With Jardine and Reid under pressure to find the killer of Anna Palaski, a link is made with another murder. Meanwhile, Taggart is sitting uncomfortably in Chief Superintendent McVitie's chair.

Jim Taggart	MARK McMANUS
Mike Jardine	JAMES MACPHERSON
Jackie Reid	BLYTHE DUFF
Supt McVitie	IAIN ANDERS
Dr Andrews	ROBERT ROBERTSON
Jean Taggart	HARRIET BUCHAN
Marjorie McVitie	MONA BRUCE
Father Doyle	GERARD MURPHY
Rory Macleod	GEORGE ANTON
Sam Archibald	DAVID ROPER
Lee Archibald	LESLEY DUFF
Harry Clyde	NORMAN GREGORY
Eddie Campbell	DEREK ANDERS
Susan Clyde	GIL BRAILEY
Dr Costello	DEREK RIDDELL
Ellen Pollock	ALICE MACDONALD

Written by Barry Appleton; Producer John G Temple
Director Richard Holthouse *Subtitled* 8857

10.00 News at Ten
With Trevor McDonald. *Subtitled*
Weather Martyn Davies 95499

10.30 Regional News; Weather .581789

10.40 Homeboy
Drama starring
Mickey Rourke
Christopher Walken
A declining boxer arrives in a seaside town looking for a chance to make the big time. He meets a small-time crook who promises to help him become successful. With Debra Feuer, Jon Polito and Thomas Quinn.
Director Michael Seresin (1988) 48746789
◆ **FILM REVIEWS pages 52-56**

12.40am Alien Nation
The First Cigar. George and Sikes are assigned to clean up the drug problem that is plaguing the Newcomers.
Stereo 2294513

1.35 Hollywood Report
News from Tinseltown. *Stereo* .9334364

2.05 The Beat
Featuring Massive Attack.
Repeated tomorrow 1.10am *Stereo* 9302646

3.00 The Album Show
The UK album chart with Lynn Parsons.
Repeated tomorrow 2.10am *Stereo* 16529

4.00 Jobfinder
Employment news. 9959616

5.20 Asian Eye
Asian news. 2048529

5.30-6.00am Morning News 32074
News reports throughout the night

BBC/ITV VARIATIONS
Regions may show different programme episodes
BBC1 WALES 5.35pm as BBC1 England **6.30** Wales Today **7.00** as BBC1 England **7.30** Winter in Wales **8.00** as BBC1 England
ANGLIA 5.40pm as Central **10.40** Film: Dirty Dozen: the Fatal Mission **12.25am** The Album Show **1.25** Hollywood Report **1.55** America's Top Ten **2.25** Donahue **3.20** Little Picture Show **4.25** The Time . . . the Place **5.00** The Munsters Today **5.30** as Central
CARLTON 5.40pm as Central **6.30** Regional News **7.00** as Central **10.40** Wayne Dobson Close Up **11.10** Live at Lighthouse **12.40** as Central **4.05** Donahue **4.55** The Time . . . the Place **5.30** as Central
GRANADA 5.40pm as Central **10.40** Film: Terror on Highway 91 **12.25am** Rolling Stones in Profile **12.40** as Carlton
HTV 5.40pm as Central **6.30** Regional News **7.00** as Central **10.40** Film: Wait Until Dark **12.40am** as Carlton
MERIDIAN 5.40pm as Central **6.00** Regional News **6.30** The Country Set **7.00** as Anglia **5.00** Freescreen **5.30** as Central
YORKSHIRE 5.40pm as Central **5.55** Regional News **6.30** Runway **7.00** as Central **10.40** Film: Farewell to the King **12.45am** The Equalizer **1.40** Hollywood Report **2.10** Videofashion **2.40** The Album Show **3.40** Noisy Mothers **4.35** Jobfinder **5.30** as Central

4 CHANNEL 4

5.50pm Terrytoons
More cartoon adventures. .598437

6.00 The Crystal Maze
Contestants face an eclectic collection of games and tasks testing their mental and physical dexterity against the clock. Host Ed Tudor-Pole guides them through the four time zones in search of the elusive crystals.
Director David Croft; Producer Malcolm Heyworth Rpt Stereo Subtitled ..42895

7.00 Channel 4 News
Presented by Jon Snow and Tanya Sillem. *Subtitled*
Followed by **Weather** 837012

7.50 The Slot
Viewers offer their opinions on events making the news. ...646128

8.00 Brookside
There are more flooding problems for the Banks and Eddie is determined to get to the bottom of it. Mike has a close call while Ron has a battle on his hands with Bev.

Eddie Banks	PAUL BROUGHTON
Rosie Banks	SUSAN TWIST
Carl Banks	STEPHEN DONALD
Sarah Banks	ANDREA MARSHALL
Jimmy Corkhill	DEAN SULLIVAN
Jackie Corkhill	SUE JENKINS
Barry Grant	PAUL USHER
D-D Dixon	IRENE MAROT
Ron Dixon	VINCE EARL
Mike Dixon	PAUL BYATT
Bev McLoughlin	SARAH WHITE
Max Farnham	STEVEN PINDER
Patricia Farnham	GABRIELLE GLAISTER
David Crosbie	JOHN BURGESS
Jean Crosbie	MARCIA ASHTON
Mick Johnson	LOUIS EMERICK
Mandy Jordache	SANDRA MAITLAND
Beth Jordache	ANNA FRIEL
Rachel Jordache	TIFFANY CHAPMAN
Sinbad	MICHAEL STARKE
Mo McGee	TINA MALONE
Audrey Manners	JUDITH BARKER
Emma Piper	PAULA BELL
Kevin	TERRY MELIA
Viv	KERRIE THOMAS
Penny Crosbie	MARY TAMM
Sam Martin	JOHN HARDING

This week's episodes written by Susan Pleat
Producer Mal Young; Director Patrick Tucker
Stereo Subtitled 7876

8.30 Travelog
CHOICE On the programme tonight, Daisy Waugh visits Corbières in the South of France, a beautiful, serene land, scattered with ruined castles. She samples some local cuisine and investigates the traditional sport of boar hunting. Meanwhile in another continent, Pete McCarthy visits Casablanca.
See today's choices.
Producer Richard Lightbody; Editor Jenny Mallinson Duff. Repeated on Friday at 4.00pm Stereo Subtitled 6383

9.00 Dispatches
Another edition in the award-winning current affairs series, combining investigation, observation and ingenuity.
Repeated tomorrow, 12.55am
Subtitled 301136

9.45 Snapshots
Actress Sheila Hancock returns to Wallingford in Oxfordshire where she was dispatched at the outbreak of war, aged 8.
Directors Eric Harwood, Josh Hall Rpt Subtitled 386708

10.00 Film premiere
The Good Mother
CHOICE Drama starring
Diane Keaton
Liam Neeson
Anna Dunlap, who has lived with her 6-year-old daughter Molly since divorcing her lawyer husband, becomes passionately involved with an Irish sculptor. But their affair is to have a profound effect on Anna's relationship with her daughter.

Anna Dunlap	DIANE KEATON
Leo Cutter	LIAM NEESON
Muth	JASON ROBARDS
Grandfather	RALPH BELLAMY
Grandmother	TERESA WRIGHT
Brian	JAMES NAUGHTON
Molly	ASIA VIEIRA
Frank Williams	JOE MORTON
Ursula	KATEY SAGAL
Aunt Rain	MARGARET BARD

Director Leonard Nimoy (1988)
Subtitled 1673
◆ **FILM REVIEWS pages 52-56**

12.00 Moviewatch
Tonight's film reviewers deliver their verdicts on *Killing Zoë, Nostradamus* and *Eat Drink Man Woman*. With Johnny Vaughan.
Shown last Friday *Stereo* 39987

12.30am LA Law
On the Toad Again. Sollers and Kelsey represent an obsessed mistress of a married man who is charged with his murder.
Stereo 61258

1.30 Jacques Loussier
The French pianist, who has combined jazz with Bach, in concert in London in 1985. Featuring André Arpino (percussion) and Vincent Charbonnier (bass). *Rpt* ..5403677

2.35-4.15am Sanders of the River
Adventure starring
Leslie Banks
Paul Robeson
While absent on leave, the British commissioner of an African colony hears that his deputy has been killed. He returns to try and suppress an uprising.

R G Sanders	LESLIE BANKS
Bosambo	PAUL ROBESON
Lilongo	NINA MAE McKINNEY
Tibbets	ROBERT COCHRAN
Ferguson	MARTIN WALKER

Director Zoltan Korda (1935) *B/W* .712074
◆ **FILM REVIEWS pages 52-56**

18•3

INFO SKILLS BOOK FOUR

4 The ◣CHOICE symbol refers the reader to more information about certain programmes.

(a) What is the earliest 'Choice' programme showing?

(b) Which TV channel has no 'Choice' programmes that evening?

5 On which pages of this edition of the *Radio Times* will you find the Film Reviews?

6 At what time does each channel's evening news programmes start?

(a) BBC1

(b) BBC2

(c) ITV

(d) Channel 4

7 If you wanted to watch all the 'soaps' shown, make a list of the starting times, programme titles and TV channels, in the order you would watch:

Time	Title	Channel

8 Which programmes would you watch if you are interested in:

(a) knowing what other viewers think of BBC TV programmes?

(b) cooking?

(c) sport?

(d) reviews of new film releases?

(e) science fiction?

(f) quiz shows?

(g) travel?

9 (*a*) What is BBC1 Wales showing at 7.30 instead of *On the Up*?

(*b*) What is Anglia TV showing at 10.40?

(*c*) What is Meridian ITV showing instead of *Home and Away*?

10 How long do these programmes last?

(*a*) *Taggart*

(*d*) *Points of View*

(*b*) *Travelog*

(*e*) *Channel 4 News*

(*c*) *Sportsnight*

(*f*) *Star Trek*

11 Who presents or introduces these programmes?

(*a*) *The Private Life of Plants*

(*b*) *Points of View*

(*c*) *All in the Mind*

(*d*) *The Late Show*

(*e*) *Sportsnight*

12 Who

(*a*) produced *Sportsnight*?

(*b*) wrote *The World at War*?

(*c*) presented *The Six O'Clock News*?

(*d*) directed *The Good Mother*?

(*e*) stars in *Star Trek: The Next Generation*?

(*f*) produced *This is Your Life*?

(*g*) edited *Travelog*?

(*h*) wrote this week's episode of *Brookside*?

Using Teletext

19

Teletext is an information system which is prepared and updated by each of the main television channels. You can also get European language teletext channels via a satellite receiver and CNN Text offers an international teletext service. Teletext is transmitted alongside normal TV broadcasts and is accessed by TV sets which have an inbuilt teletext facility (some older sets are not equipped to read Teletext).

Select ITV (Channel 3) and press the ☰ or ⓉⒺⓍⓉ button on the remote control. This will bring a page of Teletext onto the screen and will tell you the page number to dial for the contents.

To access the Contents page of Teletext, you need to key in **101** (401 on Channel 4) on the remote control.

Look at this list of Teletext pages on ITV (the page numbers and titles will change as new subjects are added and older ones are deleted):

Teletext pages on ITV

Page numbers are subject to change

1 Which pages would you call up to find out about:

(a) last week's National Lottery result?

(b) TV programmes on BBC2?

(c) the news headlines?

(d) sports results?

(e) Gatwick flight arrivals?

2 Which pages would you call up if you wanted to see:

(a) what is on TV tomorrow?

(b) the main stories in today's newspapers?

(c) the national weather forecast?

(d) what driving conditions on the motorways are like?

(e) today's holiday bargains?

3 Use Teletext to answer these questions:

(a) What were last week's jackpot National Lottery numbers?

(b) Name one event in history which took place this week

(c) What was the first flight arrival at Gatwick today?

(d) What is the first TV film reviewed in today's Teletext?

(e) What is the first main news headline today?

(f) What is the best-selling music album in today's chart?

(g) Which is the cheapest City Break holiday advertised today?

(h) What is today's Tourist Rate for changing £s into Spanish pesetas?

(i) What is the Air Quality in your part of the country today?

(j) Which page would you look on for Teletext's A-Z Index?

Which bus goes where?

Bus companies produce maps and timetables to show where their buses go. Look at the bus route map and timetable index on sheets 20.2 and 20.3, then answer these questions:

1 Which buses travel along:

(*a*) Pitmore Road?

(*b*) Brambridge Road?

(*c*) Spring Lane?

(*d*) Chestnut Avenue?

(*e*) Sandy Lane?

(*f*) Church Road?

2 In which street is the bus station?

3 The railway station is on the corner of two roads. Which ones?

4 Which buses serve:

(*a*) Whiteparish?

(*b*) Lower Upham?

(*c*) Crowd Hill?

(*d*) Stoke Common?

(*e*) Chilworth?

(*f*) Woolston?

5 Does the railway pass UNDER or OVER these roads?

(*a*) Twyford Road

(*b*) Brambridge Road

(*c*) Bournemouth Road

(*d*) Bishopstoke Road

6 Which bus would you catch if you wanted to go from:

(*a*) Eastleigh to West End?

(*b*) Eastleigh to Romsey?

(*c*) Southampton to Otterbourne?

(*d*) North Baddesley to Eastleigh?

(*e*) Hedge End to Eastleigh?

WHICH BUS GOES WHERE?

CODE   ‡—Certain buses only.   *AV214*—Alder Valley Service.

Full details of services to certain places are shown in other timetable booklets:
●—See 'South Hants' (Bishop's Waltham) booklet.   ■—See 'Wintonline' booklet.
♥—See 'South Hants' (Romsey) booklet.   ★—See 'Antonbus' booklet.
□—See 'Provincial' booklet.   ▲—See 'Wiltsway' booklets.

EVERY CARE has been taken in compiling this index, but the Company cannot be held liable for any delay or inconvenience arising from inaccuracies, alterations to services, or any other cause.

Place	Service
ALLBROOK	40, 41, 44
ALRESFORD■	*AV214*
ALTON	*AV214*
AMPFIELD	66
ANDOVER★	X12
BARTON STACEY■	X12
BASSETT	X12, 45, 45A, 46, 46A, 47, 62, *AV214*
BISHOPSTOKE	X14, 42, 42A, 43, 48, 48A, 53, 53A
BISHOP'S WALTHAM●	53, 53A‡, 69, 69A
BOYATT WOOD	40, 41, 44, 46
CHANDLER'S FORD	40, 41, 42, 42A, 43, 45, 45A, 46A, 47
CHILWORTH	62
COLDEN COMMON	44, 48, 69, 69A
COMPTON■	X12, 47, *AV214*
CROWD HILL	48, 69
DURLEY●	53, 53A‡
EASTLEIGH to	
Bishop's Waltham	53, 53A‡
Chandler's Ford	40, 41, 42, 42A, 43
Colden Common	44, 48
Fair Oak	X14, 48, 48A, 53, 53A
Hedge End	49
Hiltingbury	40, 41, 42, 42A
Horton Heath	53, 53A‡
Hypermarket	46, 53A, 65
Marwell Zoo	48‡
Moorgreen	49
North Baddesley	65
North Stoneham	48, 48A, 53, 53A, 65
Romsey	65
Southampton (Direct)	X14, 46, 48, 48A, 53
Southampton (Indirect)	49
Southampton Airport	X14, 49
Stoke Common	42, 42A
Stoke Wood	43, 48, 48A, 53, 53A
Swaythling	X14, 48, 48A, 49, 53
West End	49
Winchester	44, 48
Woolston	49
FISHERS POND	48, 69, 69A
FAIR OAK	X14, 48, 48A, 53, 53A, 69
FAREHAM□	69, 69A
FARNHAM	*AV214*
GUILDFORD	*AV214*
HEDGE END●	49
HILTINGBURY	40, 41, 42, 42A, 45, 46A‡, 66
HORTON HEATH●	53, 53A‡
HURSLEY	45A, 66
HYPERMARKET	45, 45A, 46, 46A, 47, 53A, 65
LONGPARISH★	X12

Place	Service
LOWER UPHAM	69, 69A
MARWELL ZOO	48‡, 69‡, 69A
MOORGREEN●	49
NEWTOWN●	53, 53A‡, 69, 69A
NORTH BADDESLEY♥	62, 65
NORTH STONEHAM	48, 48A, 53, 53A, 65
OAKMOUNT ESTATE	42A, 43, 46A
OTTERBOURNE	40, 41, 46A‡, 47
PORTSWOOD	X14, 48, 48A, 53
PYLEHILL	48A, 53A
ROMSEY♥	62, 65, 66
ST. CROSS■	X12, 44, 47, 48, 69, 69A, *AV214*
SALISBURY▲	66
SCRAGG HILL♥	62, 65
SOUTHAMPTON to●♥	
Alresford	*AV214*
Alton	*AV214*
Andover	X12
Barton Stacey	X12
Bishop's Waltham	53
Chandler's Ford	45, 45A, 46A, 47
Colden Common	48
Compton	X12, 47, *AV214*
Eastleigh (Direct)	X14, 46, 48, 48A, 53
Eastleigh (Indirect)	49
Fair Oak	X14, 48, 48A, 53
Farnham	*AV214*
Guildford	*AV214*
Hiltingbury	45, 46A‡
Horton Heath	53
Hursley	45A
Marwell Zoo	48‡
Otterbourne	47
Southampton Airport	X14, 49
Sutton Scotney	X12
Winchester	X12, 47, 48, *AV214*
SOUTHAMPTON AIRPORT	X14, 49
STOKE COMMON	42, 42A
STOKE WOOD	43, 48, 48A, 53, 53A
SUTTON SCOTNEY■	X12
SWANMORE●	53, 69, 69A
SWAYTHLING	X14, 48, 48A, 49, 53
TWYFORD■	44, 48, 69, 69A
VELMORE ESTATE	42A, 45A‡, 46
WEST END●	49
WHITEPARISH▲	66
WICKHAM□	69, 69A
WINCHESTER■	X12, 44, 47, 48, 66, 69, 69A, *AV214*
WOOLSTON●	49
WORTHY DOWN■	X12

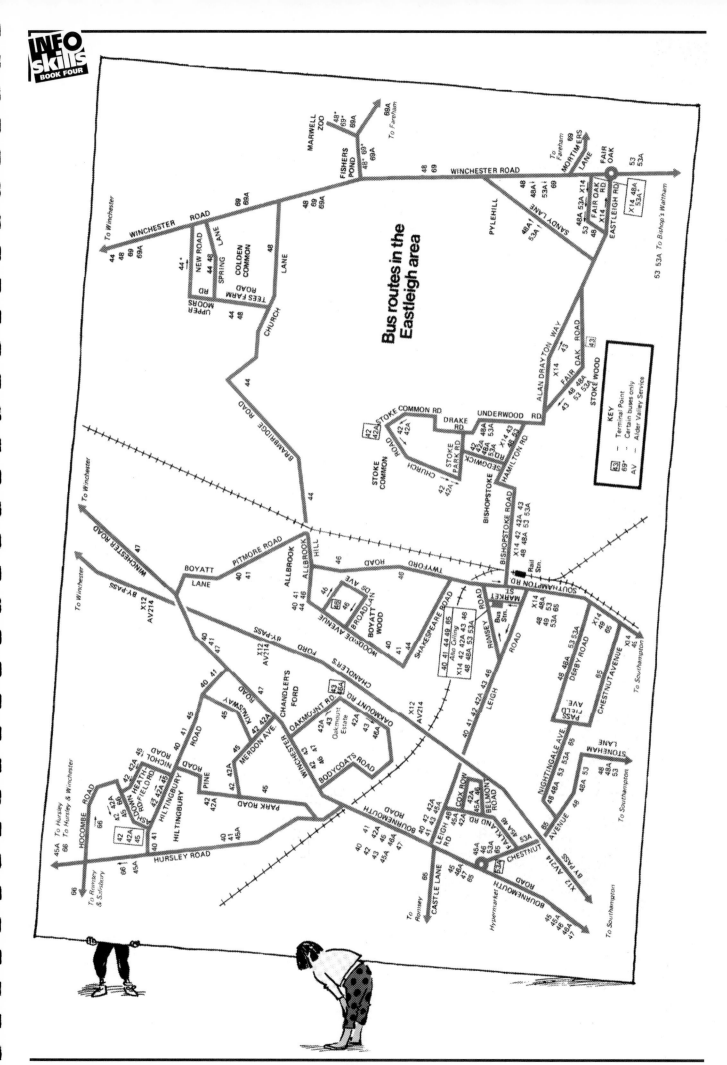

Bus routes in the Eastleigh area

Look at this timetable for bus service 44:

EASTLEIGH · WINCHESTER via Boyatt Wood, Allbrook, Colden Common and Twyford Service 44

ROUTE: 44 **From Eastleigh** via Twyford Rd., Shakespeare Rd., Woodside Ave., Allbrook Hill, Brambridge Rd., Church Lane, Tees Farm Rd., **Colden Common,** Spring Lane, A333, **Twyford,** Searles Hill, Twyford Rd., Saint Cross Rd. and Southgate St. **to Winchester.**

Including buses on Services 40/41 running between Eastleigh and Hiltingbury via Boyatt Wood.

Mondays to Saturdays		NS 44	44	NS 44	NS 69	S	41	44	41	44	41	44	NS 41	S 41	NS 41	44	44	44	44	44
EASTLEIGH (Bus Station)	⭑	0617	0717	0752		0817	0932	1032	1132	1232	1332	1432	1502	1532	1602	1632	1732	1832	2132	2232
Shakespeare Road (Arrow Inn)		0621	0721	0756		0821	0936	1036	1136	1236	1336	1436	1506	1536	1606	1636	1735	1836	2136	2236
Boyatt Wood (Bosville North)		0624	0724	0759		0824	0939	1039	1139	1239	1339	1439	1509	1539	1609	1639	1739	1839	2139	2239
Allbrook (Post Office)		0626	0726	0801		0826	0941	1041	1141	1241	1341	1441	1511	1541	1611	1641	1741	1841	2141	2241
Hiltingbury (Ashdown Road)		♥					0952		1152		1352		1522	1552	1622		♥	♥		♥
Colden Common (Spring Lane/A333)		0634	0734	0809◪	0819†	0834		1049		1249		1449				1649	1749	1849	2149	2249
Twyford (Post Office)			0738		0823	0838		1053		1253		1453				1653			2153	
St Cross (Bell Inn)			0745		0830	0845		1100		1300		1500				1700			2200	
WINCHESTER (Bus Station)	⭑		0755		0840	0855		1110		1310		1510				1710			2210	

		NS 44	NS 44	44	40	44	40	44	40	44	40	44	44	44
WINCHESTER (Bus Station)	⭑				0920		1120		1320		1520		1720	
St Cross (Bell Inn)					0930		1130		1330		1530		1730	
Twyford (Post Office)					0937		1137		1337		1537		1737	
Colden Common (Spring Lane/A333)		0636	0726	0822	0941		1141		1341		1541		1741	1851	2251
Hiltingbury (Ashdown Road)						1038		1238		1438		1638		
Allbrook (Post Office)		0644	0734	0830	0949	1049	1149	1249	1349	1449	1549	1649	1749	1859	2259
Boyatt Wood (Bosville North)		0646	0736	0832	0951	1051	1151	1251	1351	1451	1551	1651	1751	1901	2301
Shakespeare Road (Arrow Inn)		0649	0739	0835	0954	1054	1154	1254	1354	1454	1554	1654	1754	1904	2304
EASTLEIGH (Bus Station)	⭑	0653	0743	0839●	0958	1058	1158	1258	1358	1458	1558	1658	1758	1908	2308

Sundays

		44	44	44	44
EASTLEIGH (Bus Station)	⭑	1055	1255	1555	1755
Shakespeare Road (Arrow Inn)		1059	1259	1559	1759
Boyatt Wood (Bosville North)		1101	1301	1601	1801
Allbrook (Post Office)		1103	1303	1603	1803
COLDEN COMMON (Spring Lane/A333)		1109♥	1309♥	1609♥	1809♥

		44	44	44	44
COLDEN COMMON (Spring Lane/A333)		1111	1311	1611	1811
Allbrook (Post Office)		1117	1317	1617	1817
Boyatt Wood (Bosville North)		1119	1319	1619	1819
Shakespeare Road (Arrow Inn)		1121	1321	1621	1821
EASTLEIGH (Bus Station)	⭑	1125	1325	1625	1825

CODE
S—Sats only.
NS—Not Sats.

♥—In Colden Common runs via Upper Moors Rd., New Rd. and A333 to Spring Lane.
●—On schooldays continues at 0843 to Toynbee School, arrive 0850.

◪—Change to connecting bus.
†—Time at Parish Hall, not Spring Lane/A333.
⭑—Rail Station nearby.

1 Look at the ROUTE listed at the top of the timetable and write down the next stop after:

(a) Woodside Avenue

(b) Colden Common

(c) Twyford Road

2 What does NS mean?

3 What does S mean?

4 (a) What time does the first bus leave Eastleigh?

(b) What time does the first bus leave Winchester?

(c) What time does the first bus from Eastleigh to Winchester leave?

(d) What time does the last bus leave Eastleigh?

(e) Where does it finish its journey?

5 If you want to get to Winchester by 0855:

(a) What number bus do you catch?

(b) What time does it leave Allbrook?

6 Where do the service 41 buses end their journeys?

7 (a) How many number 44 buses go from Winchester to Eastleigh each day?

(b) How often do they go?

8 What is the latest time you could catch a bus from Colden Common to Eastleigh?

9 If you were in Winchester and wanted to get to Twyford by lunch-time, what time would you catch the bus?

10 How long does the journey from Eastleigh to Winchester take?

11 Use the timetable to plan the following journey:

> Leave home on the first bus to Hiltingbury from Eastleigh to visit your cousin. After spending a couple of hours there, return to Eastleigh on the next bus. Have lunch there and then catch the next bus to Winchester to do some shopping. After two hours, catch the next bus back to Eastleigh.

Route Planner

From	Bus number	Leave at	To	Arrive at
Eastleigh				

Do you know how to work out times written in the 24-hour way? If you do, have a go at writing times in the normal way like this:

0715 → 7.15 a.m.

1230 → 12.30 p.m.

1400 → 2.00 p.m.

1730 → 5.30 p.m.

(a.m. = morning   p.m. = afternoon)

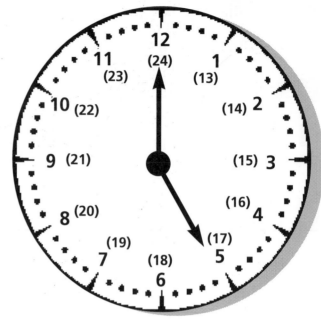

1 1500

2 1600

3 1430

4 1630

5 1800

6 0340

7 1030

8 0600

9 1845

10 2220

Now write these times in the 24-hour way - but watch the a.m. and p.m. signs!

6.30 p.m. → 1830

6.30 a.m. → 0630

11 5.00 a.m.

12 5.00 p.m.

13 2.30 p.m.

14 1.00 a.m.

15 7.40 p.m.

16 7.30 a.m.

17 1.55 p.m.

18 9.05 a.m.

19 11.30 p.m.

20 4.15 p.m.

The railway companies produce route maps of their services, just like bus companies do. Look at this route map of part of the southern region rail network (the numbers beside each route tell you which **timetable number** to look up.):

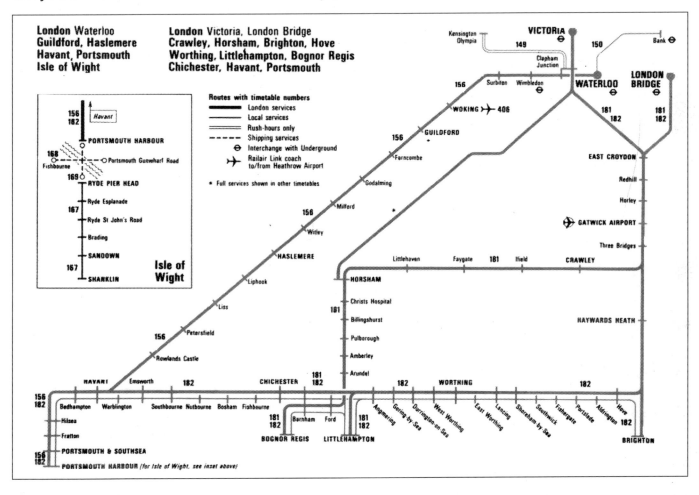

London Waterloo
Guildford, Haslemere
Havant, Portsmouth
Isle of Wight

London Victoria, London Bridge
Crawley, Horsham, Brighton, Hove
Worthing, Littlehampton, Bognor Regis
Chichester, Havant, Portsmouth

Routes with timetable numbers
━━━ London services
─── Local services
═══ Rush-hours only
- - - Shipping services
⊖ Interchange with Underground
✈ Railair Link coach to/from Heathrow Airport

* Full services shown in other timetables

1 Write down the number of the timetable you would look up to find these services:

(a) Haslemere to Guildford [ ]

(d) Waterloo to Bank [ ]

(b) Crawley to Horsham [ ]

(e) Fratton to Portsmouth Harbour [ ]

(c) Havant to Chichester [ ]

(f) Sandown to Shanklin [ ]

2 Which timetable shows the Railair Link to Heathrow Airport? [ ]

3 Which stations are served by

(a) a local service only? [ ]   (b) a rush-hour service only? [ ]

4 What do you think the 'wavy line' symbol between Portsmouth and Ryde stands for?

[ ]

Each rail timetable also contains an **index** to all the stations. Here is part of one of them:

Notes of facilities.
Catering — Travellers-Fare or equivalent
Disabled — Disabled 'core' station (see page 3)
Parcels — Rail Express Parcels/Red Star
Rail Drive — Godfrey Davis self-drive car hire
Trolleys — Passenger self-help trolleys
Underground — Station also served by London Regional Transport
★ — indicates that facility is available

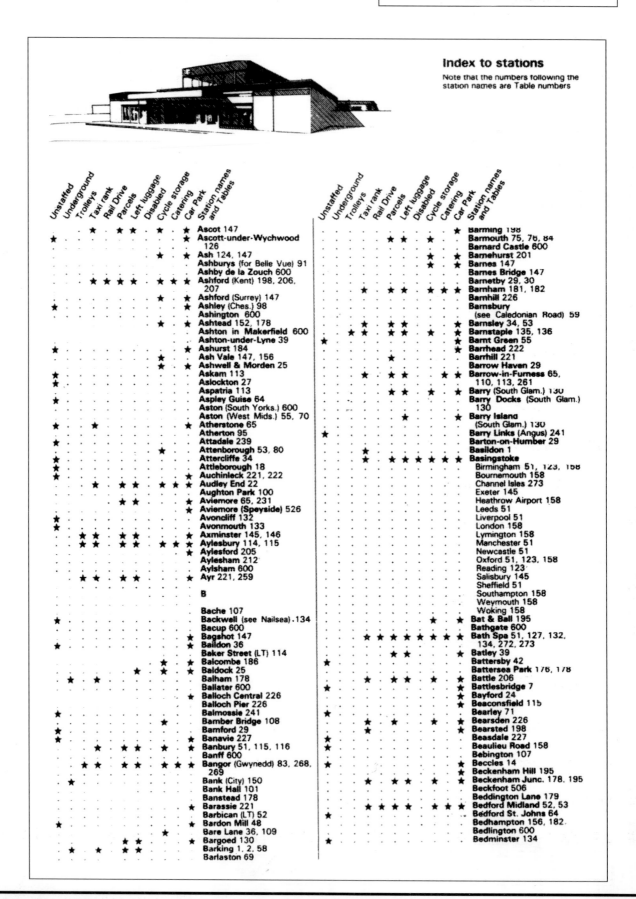

Index to stations

Note that the numbers following the station names are Table numbers

Ascot 147
Ascott-under-Wychwood 126
Ash 124, 147
Ashburys (for Belle Vue) 91
Ashby de la Zouch 600
Ashford (Kent) 198, 206, 207
Ashford (Surrey) 147
Ashley (Ches.) 98
Ashington 600
Ashtead 152, 178
Ashton in Makerfield 600
Ashton-under-Lyne 39
Ashurst 184
Ash Vale 147, 156
Ashwell & Morden 25
Askam 113
Aslockton 27
Aspatria 113
Aspley Guise 64
Aston (South Yorks.) 600
Aston (West Mids.) 55, 70
Atherstone 65
Atherton 95
Attadale 239
Attenborough 53, 80
Attercliffe 34
Attleborough 18
Auchinleck 221, 222
Audley End 22
Aughton Park 100
Aviemore 65, 231
Aviemore (Speyside) 526
Avoncliff 132
Avonmouth 133
Axminster 145, 146
Aylesbury 114, 115
Aylesford 205
Aylesham 212
Aylsham 600
Ayr 221, 259

B

Bache 107
Backwell (see Nailsea) 134
Bacup 600
Bagshot 147
Baildon 36
Baker Street (LT) 114
Balcombe 186
Baldock 25
Balham 178
Ballater 600
Balloch Central 226
Balloch Pier 226
Balmossie 241
Bamber Bridge 108
Barnford 29
Banavie 227
Banbury 51, 115, 116
Banff 600
Bangor (Gwynedd) 83, 268, 269
Bank (City) 150
Bank Hall 101
Banstead 178
Barassie 221
Barbican (LT) 52
Bardon Mill 48
Bare Lane 36, 109
Bargoed 130
Barking 1, 2, 58
Barlaston 69

Barming 198
Barmouth 75, 76, 84
Barnard Castle 600
Barnehurst 201
Barnes 147
Barnes Bridge 147
Barnetby 29, 30
Barnham 181, 182
Barnhill 226
Barnsbury (see Caledonian Road) 59
Barnsley 34, 53
Barnstaple 135, 136
Barnt Green 55
Barrhead 222
Barrhill 221
Barrow Haven 29
Barrow-in-Furness 65, 110, 113, 261
Barry (South Glam.) 130
Barry Docks (South Glam.) 130
Barry Island (South Glam.) 130
Barry Links (Angus) 241
Barton-on-Humber 29
Basildon 1
Basingstoke
Birmingham 51, 123, 158
Bournemouth 158
Channel Isles 273
Exeter 145
Heathrow Airport 158
Leeds 51
Liverpool 51
London 158
Lymington 158
Manchester 51
Newcastle 51
Oxford 51, 123, 158
Reading 123
Salisbury 145
Sheffield 51
Southampton 158
Weymouth 158
Woking 158
Bat & Ball 195
Bathgate 600
Bath Spa 51, 127, 132, 134, 272, 273
Batley 39
Battersby 42
Battersea Park 176, 178
Battle 206
Battlesbridge 7
Bayford 24
Beaconsfield 115
Bearley 71
Bearsden 226
Bearsted 198
Beasdale 227
Beaulieu Road 158
Bebington 107
Beccles 14
Beckenham Hill 195
Beckenham Junc. 178, 195
Beckfoot 506
Beddington Lane 179
Bedford Midland 52, 53
Bedford St. Johns 64
Bedhampton 156, 182
Badlington 600
Bedminster 134

5 In which timetables will you find train services to these stations?

(*a*) Beccles ⬚

(*b*) Ballater ⬚

(*c*) Basildon ⬚

(*d*) Aspley Guise ⬚

(*e*) Battle ⬚

(*f*) Avonmouth ⬚

(*g*) Beaulieu Road ⬚

(*h*) Southampton ⬚

6 Which town in the index has the largest number of train services? ⬚

7 Could you park your car at Baldock station? ⬚

8 Could you get something to eat at Aylesbury station? ⬚

How do you know? ⬚

9 Which stations have facilities for disabled people? ⬚

10 Could you hire a car from these stations?

	YES	NO		YES	NO
(*a*) Bath Spa	⬚	⬚	(*d*) Bangor	⬚	⬚
(*b*) Aylesbury	⬚	⬚	(*e*) Axminster	⬚	⬚
(*c*) Bedford Midland	⬚	⬚	(*f*) Ashford	⬚	⬚

11 Which stations are served by the London Underground?

⬚

12 Which station would you find in timetable 24? ⬚

13 Could you collect a Red Star parcel from these stations?

	YES	NO		YES	NO
(*a*) Battle	⬚	⬚	(*d*) Ascot	⬚	⬚
(*b*) Baldock	⬚	⬚	(*e*) Bamber Bridge	⬚	⬚
(*c*) Barnham	⬚	⬚	(*f*) Audley End	⬚	⬚

14 Could you get a taxi from Barking? ⬚

15 If a new station was opened at Barnholme, which station would it come after in the index?

⬚

Planning a rail journey

The railway timetable gives details of services from London Waterloo to Bournemouth and also the return journey (Table 158). Because there are so many trains on these services the timetable lasts for about twenty-three pages! The timetable also shows journeys from London to Salisbury and Exeter (Table 145) and from Salisbury, Southampton, Eastleigh and Fareham to Portsmouth (Table 165).

Here are parts of those timetables showing some of the Saturday train services:

Table 158
London, Basingstoke and Southampton to Bournemouth — Saturdays

		J			J	E		A	①		J ①		B ①	①	C ☆☆		E ☆☆		J ①	A
London Waterloo ⊖	152, 156 d		05 45		06 12	06 45	06 50	07 12	07 45	07 42	08 12	08 35		08 45		08 42	09 10	09 12	09 35
Surbiton	152, 156 d		05 39		06 28	06 39		07 28	07 37	07 50	08 28			08 37		08 58	09 07	09 28	
406 Heathrow Airport ✈	d													08 10					
Woking	156 d		06 10		06 43	07 10	07 17	07 43	08 10	08 13	08 43			09 10		09 13	09 36	09 43	
Brookwood	156 d				06 48			07 48		08 18	08 48					09 18		09 48	
Farnborough (Main)	d				06 55			07 55		08	09 00					09 25		09 55	
Fleet	d				07 00			08 00		08 30	09 00					09 30		10 00	
Winchfield	d				07 05			08 05		08 35	09 05					09 35		10 05	
Hook	d				07 08			08 08		08 38	09 08					09 38		10 08	
Basingstoke	d		06 32	07 02	07a15	07 32	07a38	07 43	08a15	08 23	08 32	08a15	09 28	09 32	09 45	09a48	09a57	10a15	10 21
Micheldever	← d			07 12				07 55			08 58				09 58				
Winchester	d		06 49	07 21		07 49		08 04	08 43	08 49	09 07		09 46	09 49	10 04	10 07			10 43
Shawford	d			07 26				08 09			09 12				10 12				
Eastleigh	d	06 45	06 58	07 32		07 58		08 18	08a52	08 59	09 17		09 55		10 07	10 19			10a52
Southampton Airport	d		07 02	07 35		08 02		08 18		09 02	09 21			10 02					
Swaythling	d	06 49		07 38				08 20		09 23					10 23				
St. Denys	165 d	06 52		07 41				08 23		09 26					10 26				
Southampton	165 a	06 57	07 10	06 57	07 46		08 10	08 29		09 10	09 32	09 45	09 32	10 04	10 10	10 25	10 34		10 45
Southampton	165 d	07 15	07 14	07 49		08 13		08 47		09 13	09 48	09 45	09 48	10 05	10 13	10 26	10 48		10 45
Millbrook (Hants)	d		07 18	07 49				08 49					09 50						
Redbridge	165 d		07 21	07 52				08 52					09 53						
Totton	d		07 23	07 54				08 54					09 55						
Lyndhurst Road	d		07 27	07 59				08 59					10 00						
Beaulieu Road	d		07 31	08 03				09 03					10 04						
Brockenhurst	a		07 29	07 38	08 09		08 28	09 09			09 28			10 10	10 19	10 28			
160 Lymington Town	a		07 49			08 49		09p19			09 49			10p19		10 49			
160 Lymington Pier	a		07 51			08 51		09p21			09 51			10p21		10 51			
Yarmouth Slipway	Ship a		08 30					09 30		10x00			10 30			11p00		11 30	
Brockenhurst	d		07 29	08 10		08 28		09 10			09 28			10 10	10 19	10 28			
Sway	d			08 15				09 15						10 15					
New Milton	d		07 36	08 20		08 36		09 20			09 36			10 20	10 27	10 36			
Hinton Admiral	d			08 24				09 24						10 24					
Christchurch	d		07 44	08 29		08 44		09 29			09 44			10 29	10 35	10 44			
Pokesdown	d			08 32				09 32						10 32					
Bournemouth	a		07 51	08 36		08 51		09 36			09 51		10 13	10 36	10 41	10 51	11 00			11 13

For general notes see front of book

A From Reading (Table 123) to Portsmouth Harbour (Table 165)
B 28 May and 25 June to 24 September from Wolverhampton dep. 08 49. From 8 October from Liverpool Lime Street dep. 07 20 to Poole (Table 51)
C From Derby dep. 06 00 to Poole (Table 51)
D 23 July to 3 September
E To Exeter St. David's (Table 145)
G To Salisbury (Table 145)
H 28 May to 24 September
J To Weymouth (Table 159)
K Until 3 September
L Until 1 October. From Liverpool Lime Street dep. 07 50 to Poole (Table 51)

b Arr. 5 minutes earlier
n Until 1 October
p Until 3 September
q From 10 September
r Until 3 September arr. 11 47. Passengers can arrive Southampton 11 36 by changing at St. Denys
t Until 29 October 6 minutes later
v Until 1 October 4 minutes later
x Until 1 October arr. 13 46

729

---

1 (a) What time does the first train leave Waterloo?

   (b) What time does it arrive in Bournemouth?

   (c) How long does the journey take?

   (d) What time does the train stop in Eastleigh?

   (e) What time does it arrive in Southampton?

   (f) How long does the journey from Eastleigh to Southampton take?

Table 158

Bournemouth to Southampton, Basingstoke and London

		K							G	B		J	H	E
Bournemouth	d	00 01				05 54		06 18		06 50	06 54	07 15	07 41	
Pokesdown	d							06 22			06 58	07 18		
Christchurch	d	00 10				06 00		06 26			07 02	07 23		
Hinton Admiral	d					06 05					07 07	07 27		
New Milton	d	00 19				06 11	06 33				07 12	07 31		
Sway	d					06 16					07 18	07 35		
Brockenhurst	a	00 27				06 20	06 40		07 07	07 22	07 40			
Yarmouth Slipway	Ship d													06k40
160 Lymington Pier	d						06 26		06 55					07 58
160 Lymington Town	d						06 26		06 57					08 00
Brockenhurst	d	00 33				06 21	06 41		07 08	07 23	07 41			
Beaulieu Road	d										07 47			08 17
Lyndhurst Road	d					06 29					07 51			08 21
Totton	d					06 34					07 57			08 25
Redbridge	165 d					06 36					07 59			08 28
Millbrook (Hants)	d					06 39					08 03			08 31
Southampton	165 a	00 49				06 42	06 56		07 26	07 37	08 05	08 09	08 05	08 34
Southampton	165 d	01 20	05 19		05 46	06 03	06 43	06 56	07 13	07 27	07 39	08 13	08 09	08 13	08 35
St. Denys	165 d		05a28	05 37	05a55	06a12	06 17	06 51		07 17				08 17	08 41
Swaythling	d			05 40			06 20	06 54		07 21				08 21	08 44
Southampton Airport	d							06 56							
Eastleigh	d	01 40		05 45			06 25	07a00		07 26	07 47	07 52		08 26	08a48
Shawford	d			05 50			06 30		07 07	07 31				08 31	
Winchester	d	01e54		05a55			06 35		07 16	07 36	08 01			08 36	
Micheldever	d						06 44			07 45					
Basingstoke	d	02a12	02a31		05 56	06 26	06 56		07 26	07 34	07 50	07 56	08a01	08 19	08 39	08 56	09 01
Hook	d				06 02	06 32		07 32		08 02		08 32			
Winchfield	d				06 06	06 36		07 36		08 06		08 36		09 06	
Fleet	d				06 14	06 44		07 14	07 44		08 14		08 44		09 18	
Farnborough (Main)	d				06 18	06 48		07 18	07 48		08 18		08 48		09 18	
Brookwood	156 d				06 25	06 55		07 25	07 55		08 25		08 55		09 25	
Woking	156 a	02 54			06 31	07 01		07 31		08 01	08 10	08 31	08 39	09 01	09 01	09 31	09 21
406 Heathrow Airport	a								08 55		09 55		09 55		
Surbiton	152, 156 a	03 20		06 45	07 15		07 45	08 15		08 38	08 45	09 08		09 15	09 38	09 45	09 45
London Waterloo	152, 156 a	03 45		07 03	07 31		08 01	08 31	08 17	08 38	09 01	09 04	09 18	09 31	09 28	10 01	09 48

2 (a) What time does the first stopping train ('slow' train) from Basingstoke to Bournemouth leave?

(b) What time does it arrive in Bournemouth?

(c) How long does the journey take?

(d) How much longer does it take than the earlier 'fast' train?

3 (a) How long does the 0835 from London take to complete its journey?

(b) How much faster is this than the 0545?

4 (a) What time does the first train from Bournemouth leave?

(b) What is its destination?

(c) What time does it arrive there?

(d) How long does the journey take?

(e) Why does it take so long?

Table 145

London to Salisbury and Exeter

> For principal services from London
> Paddington to Exeter see Table 135

			A	C H			C A			
London Waterloo ⊖ ..	158 d	23p12 01 40	..	05 45 06 50 07 45 08 37 09 10	..	10 10 11 10	12 10 12 10 13 10 14 10 15 10 16 10	..	17 10
156 Surbiton ..	d	23p28	..	05 39 06 39 07 37	09 07	10 07 11 07	12 07 12 07 13 07 14 07 15 07 16 07	..	17 07
400 Heathrow Airport ✈ ..	d	..	..	08 10	09 10 10x40	11 10 11 40 12x40 13x40 14x40 15x40	..	16x40
Woking ..	158 d	23p43 02 10	06 10 07 17 08 10	09 36	10 38 11 36	12 38 12 39 13 36 14 38 15 36 16 38	..	17 36
123 Reading ..	d	23p00	06 26 06 53 07 53	09 19	09 53 10t53	11 53 11 53 13 25 13 53 14 53 16 14	..	16 53
Basingstoke ..	158 d	00 18	07 00 07 40 08 34	09 58	11 01 11 58 12 05	13 01 13 04 13 58 15 01 15 58 17 01	..	17 58
Overton ..	d		07 10 07 50 08 44		11 12 12 15	13 11 15 12 17 12	..	
Whitchurch (Hants) ..	d		07 16 07 56 08 50		11 19 12 21	13 17 17 19	..	
Andover ..	d	00 40 02 58	07 25 08 06 08 59	10 16	11 31 12 16 12 30	13 28 13 30 14 16 15 31 16 16 17 30	..	18 16
Grateley ..	d		07 34 08 14 09 08		11 40 12 39	13 37 13 39 15 40 17 39	..	
Salisbury ..	a	00 58 03 25	07 47 08 26 09 21 09 54 10 34	11 53 12 34 12 52	13 52 13 52 14 34 15 34 16 34 17 52	..	18 34
182 Brighton ..	d		06 32 08 20 09 20 09 20	09 32	11 32	13 32	15 32
165 Portsmouth & Southsea ..	d		07 00 08 14 09 02 10 02 10 02	11 14	13 14	15 14	17 14
165 Southampton ..	d		07 52 08 55 09 55 10 53 10 53	11 55	13 55	15 55	17 55
Salisbury ..	d	03 33	06 32 08 39 09 57 10 39 11 25 11 25	12 39	14 39 16 39	18 39
Tisbury ..	d		06 48 08 55 10 55	12 55	14 55 16 55	18 55
Gillingham (Dorset) ..	d	04b08	06 59 09 07 13 07	13 07	15 09 17 06	19 06
Sherborne ..	d	04c32	07 14 09 21 10 36 11 21 12 07 12 07	13 21	15 21 17 21	19 21
Yeovil Junction ..	d	04d40	07 23 09 28 10 44 11 28 12 07 12 07	13 28	15 29 17 28	19 28
Crewkerne ..	d		07 33 09 38 11 38	13 38	15 38 17 38	19 38
Axminster ..	d		07 50 09 54 11 08 11 54 12 30 12 36	13 54	15 54 17 54 18 33 19 54
Honiton ..	d	07 15 08 04	10 07 11 25 12 07 12 45 12 51	14 07	16 07 18 07 18h55 20 07
Feniton ..	d	07 21 08 11	10 14 12 14		19 01 20 14
Whimple ..	d	07 27 08 16	10 19		19 07
Pinhoe ..	d	07 34 08 25	10 28		
Exeter Central ..	a	07 41 08 30	10 33 11 44 12 29 13 03 13 10	14 27	16 29 18 26 19 18 20 2v
Exeter St. David's ..	a	07 45 08 35	10 38 11 50 12 35 13 08 13 15	14 32	16 34 18 31 19 24 20 34
135 Paignton ..	a	08c45 10e20	11g40 13 01 14 00 14 18 14 23	16 20	18m20 20 20 21 01 21v59
135 Plymouth ..	a	09c23 10e17	12g08 12 52 14 10 14 22 14 41	16 00	17n57 19q52 21 02 22 18

Table 165

Salisbury, Southampton, Eastleigh and Fareham to Portsmouth

		L	A	B		B	A		Q	A		U		A	B J			V	A	
Salisbury ..	d	16 09		16 31 16 44		17 24		17 44		18 24		18 44		19 39 19 50		20 39			21 38		22 20
Dean ..	d			16 58				17 58				18 58		20 04					21 50		22 34
Dunbridge ..	d			17 04				18 04				19 04		20 10					21 58		22 40
Romsey ..	d			17 09		17 44		18 09				19 09		19 59 20 16		20 59			22 03		22v48
Redbridge ..	158 d			17 17				18 17				19 17		20 24					22 11		22 56
Southampton ..	158 x	16 40		17 00 17 22		17 55		18 22		18 54		19 22		20 20 20 29		21 21			22 16		23 01
		16 44		17 03 17 23		17 56		18 23		18 55		19 29		20 15 20 29		21 15 21 29			22 18		23 02
St. Denys ..	158 d			17 29				18 29				19 29		20 36		21 36			22 23		23 10
Bitterne ..	d			17 32				18 32				19 32		20 38		21 38			22 26		23 13
Woolston ..	d			17 36				18 36				19 36		20 42		21 42			22 30		23 16
Sholing ..	d			17 38				18 38				19 38		20 45		21 45			22 32		23 18
Netley ..	d			17 42				18 42				19 42		20 49		21 49			22 36		23 22
Hamble ..	d			17 44				18 44				19 44		20 51		21 51			22 38		23 24
Bursledon ..	d			17 48				18 48				19 48		20 54		21 54			22 42		23 26
Swanwick ..	d			17 52				18 52				19 52		20 59		21 59			22 46		23 30
Eastleigh ..	d		17 03			18 03			19 03		20 03			21 03			22 03		23 03
Botley ..	d		17 11			18 11			19 11		20 11			21 11			22 11		23-11
Fareham ..	d	17 10 17 22 17 28 17 59		18 20 18 25 18 59		19 21 19 26 19 59 20 22 20 38 21 05 21 22		21 38 22 05 22 22 22 52 23 22 23 36
Portchester ..	d	17 27	18 04		18 30 19 04	19 31 20 04 20 27	21 27 22 12 22 27 22 57 23 27 23 42
Cosham ..	d	17 32	18 09		18 29 18 35 19 09	19 30 19 36 20 09 20 32	21 15 21 32 21 46 22 15 22 32 23 02 23 32 23 46
Hilsea ..	166, 182 d																				
Fratton ..	166, 182 a	17 40	18 17		18 42 19 17	19 43 20 17 20 40	21 23 21 40 22 22 40 23 02 23 40 23 54
Portsmouth & Southsea ..	166, 182 a	17 43 17 45 18 20		18 38 18 45 19 19	19 46 20 20 20 43	21 56 22 22 43 23 05 23 43 23 57
Portsmouth Harbour ..	166, 182 a	17 46 17 52 18 24		18 43 18 49 19 24	19 50 20 47 21 00 21 47	22 00 22 30 22 47 23 16 23 46 00 01

For general notes see front of book

A From Reading (Tables 123 and 158)
B From Bristol Temple Meads (Table 132)
C From Cardiff Central (Table 132)
D Until 14 January
E From 21 January
G Until 3 September. From Cardiff Central dep. 09 50 to Weymouth (Tables 132 and 159)

H Until 25 June and from 3 September from Bristol Temple Meads dep. 11 10, 2 July to 27 August from Cardiff Central dep. 10 15 (Table 132)
J Until 1 October. From Cardiff Central (Table 132)
K From 8 October: From Cardiff Central (Table 132)
L From Penzance dep. 10 45 (Tables 145 and 182)
Q From Cardiff Central dep. 16 10, 16 15 from 8 October to Brighton

U From Westbury (Table 132)
V From Weston-super-Mare dep 19 40 (Table 132)
Y From 21 January is through train from London Waterloo dep. 02 45 (Table 158)
Z 18 June to 17 September. From Leeds dep. 22 21 (Friday) (Table 51)

D Arr. 3 minutes earlier.
e Arr. 5 minutes earlier

> From time to time it is necessary to undertake extensive engineering work at weekends. This frequently affects Saturday night/ Sunday services and passengers are advised to look for specific announcements of possible diversion and delays, making a final check at stations or telephone enquiry bureaux.

756

5 If you wanted to get to Heathrow Airport by 10 o'clock, which train would you catch from Bournemouth?

6 What time does the first train serving refreshments leave Bournemouth?

7 Where has the train which leaves Bournemouth at 0741 just come from?

8 A train arrives in Bournemouth at 1100, heading for Poole. Where has it come from and what time did it set out on its journey?

9 If you were travelling from Brockenhurst to Southampton, which train would you have to catch to get there by half past seven?

10 Use the four timetables on sheets 24.1, 24.2 and 24.3 to help you plan the following journey:

> You live five minutes' walk away from Southampton railway station. You are going to pick up a new camcorder from Videotronics in Station Road, Basingstoke, at 9 o'clock on Saturday morning. You are then going to travel on to Salisbury, aiming to arrive there just after half past ten, to take some video footage of the cathedral. You are also going to visit a friend's for lunch and do some shopping in the afternoon. You are then going to catch a train to visit another friend in Romsey, to get you there just after five o'clock. After spending a couple of hours there, you want to get back to Southampton in time to watch your favourite TV programme at 7.30 pm.

Complete this journey planner:

From	To	Depart (time)	Train timetable number	Arrive (time)
1 Southampton	Basingstoke			
2 Basingstoke				
3				
4				

Members of the Automobile Association (AA) receive a copy of the *AA Handbook*, which contains lots of information about travelling by car. It contains a road atlas, a large 'Directory' of AA shops and AA-appointed hotels and maps of motorway journeys. Look at this contents page from one edition of the *AA Handbook*:

Contents

1 What can you read about on:

(a) page 17?

(b) page 96?

(c) page 21?

(d) page 15?

(e) page 27?

2 On which pages will you find information about:

(a) Communications?

(d) AA Callsafe?

(b) Relay Plus?

(e) Security?

(c) First aid?

3 Write down the pages you would turn to for help in these situations:

(a) You are thinking of taking the car abroad on next year's holiday.

(b) You want to listen to Roadwatch for news of roadworks on the route you are taking.

(c) You want help with finding the best route from your home to Exeter.

(d) You need to find a suitable hotel when you arrive.

(e) You need to do something to keep the family occupied on the journey.

4 On which page in the atlas section of the *AA Handbook* do the town plans begin?

5 Which plans begin on page 74?

The *AA Handbook* has a road atlas section at the back. Like other road atlases, you find the map you want by looking at the 'key', which is a map of the whole of Britain, divided into rectangular sections. The numbers inside each rectangle tell you the page on which you will find a detailed map of that area. Some much smaller areas, like large cities, have a whole page to themselves in the map section.

Here is the road atlas key from one edition of the *AA Handbook*:

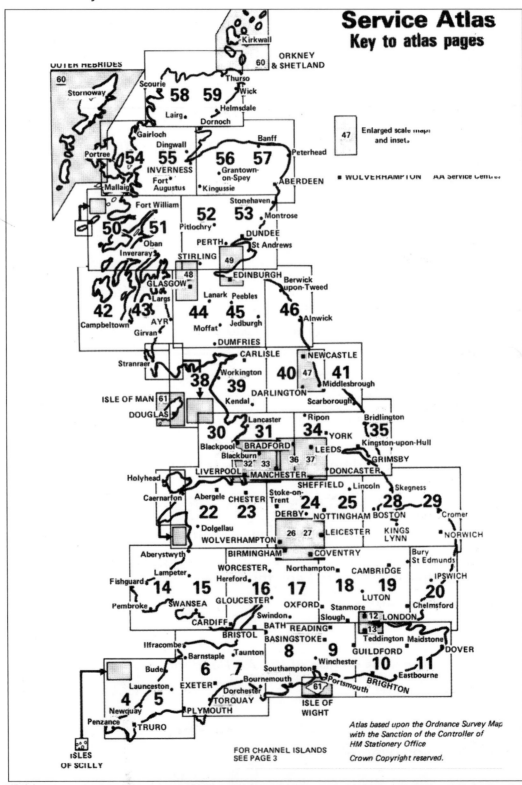

Use the atlas key on sheet 26•1 to help you answer these questions:

1 How many map pages are shown on this atlas key?

2 On which pages will you find maps of:

(*a*) Glasgow?

(*b*) London?

(*c*) Newcastle?

(*d*) Edinburgh?

(*e*) Birmingham?

3 Which other area of Britain shares a page with the Isle of Wight?

4 Is the Isle of Wight in the north or south of this map?

5 On which page will you find the Channel Islands?

6 On which page will you find the Isles of Scilly?

7 Which town on this map is furthest north?

8 Which large town will you find on page 32?

9 Why are some towns written in block capitals?

10 Write down the numbers of the pages on which you will find maps showing these towns:

(*a*) Dover

(*b*) Truro

(*c*) Swansea

(*d*) Norwich

(*e*) York

(*f*) Southampton

(*g*) Aberdeen

(*h*) Chester

(*i*) Inverness

(*j*) Oxford

Using a road atlas

Here is a section from the maps pages in the *AA Handbook*, showing the area around Norwich:

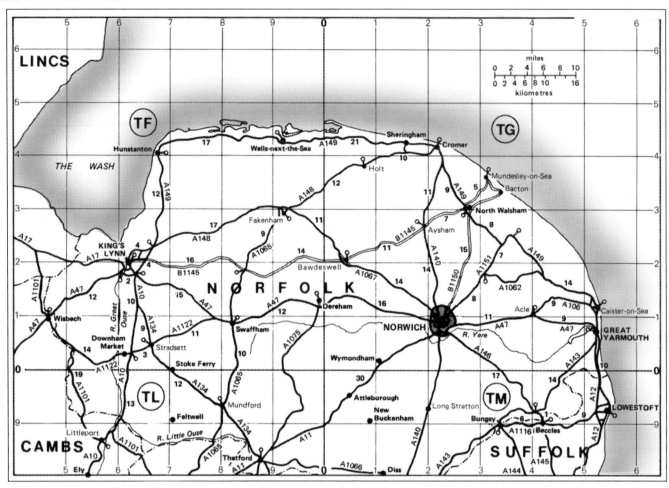

County names are in large block capitals. Important towns are in block capitals. Other towns are written in ordinary type. Road numbers (such as A47) are shown beside the roads. Distance in miles are given between places marked with a 'pin' ⊤ .

Use the information on the map to answer these questions:

1 What is the largest town shown on the map?

2 Which county occupies most of the map?

3 What is the stretch of water north of King's Lynn called?

4 If you travel from Norwich to Great Yarmouth, in which direction are you going?

5 If you want to go from Great Yarmouth to Lowestoft,

(a) which road will you use?

(b) how far is it?

(c) in which direction will you be travelling?

27•1

6 How far is it from:

(a) Norwich to Dereham?

(b) Lowestoft to Beccles?

(c) Norwich to North Walsham?

(d) Dereham to Swaffham?

(e) North Walsham to Cromer?

(f) Fakenham to Holt?

(g) Wisbech to Downham Market?

(h) Great Yarmouth to Norwich?

7 To work out your last answer what did you have to do?

8 Which road would you travel on from:

(a) Norwich to Wymondham?

(b) Beccles to Bungay?

(c) Swaffham to Dereham?

(d) Cromer to Sheringham?

(e) Downham Market to Ely?

(f) North Walsham to Mundesley-on-Sea?

(g) Fakenham to King's Lynn?

9 Which river reaches the sea at King's Lynn?

10 Make a list of the roads you would use and the total distance you would travel if you went from:

Norwich ➝ Cromer ➝
Fakenham ➝ Bawdeswell ➝
Norwich

To give someone the exact 'address' of a town, you need to look at the **grid lines** (squares) which cover the map.

This is the 'address' or **map reference** for Norwich:

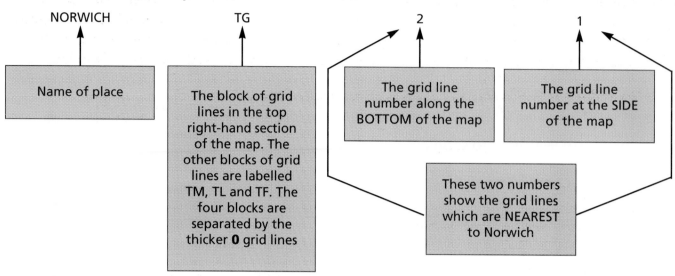

NORWICH   TG   2   1

| Name of place | The block of grid lines in the top right-hand section of the map. The other blocks of grid lines are labelled TM, TL and TF. The four blocks are separated by the thicker **0** grid lines | The grid line number along the BOTTOM of the map | The grid line number at the SIDE of the map |

These two numbers show the grid lines which are NEAREST to Norwich

So Norwich's map reference is **TG 21**.

When you write the last two digits (the nearest grid lines), the grid line on the BOTTOM of the map is always written first!

BRAIN BOX

11   Use the information on the map to write down the map references of these towns:

(a) North Walsham

(b) Cromer

(c) King's Lynn

(d) Downham Market

(e) Beccles

12   Which towns will you find near these map references?

(a) TG 10

(b) TG 41

(c) TL 79

(d) TG 01

(e) TM 19

(f) TF 81

(g) TF 70

(h) TF 74

(i) TM 29

(j) TF 93

Using a gazetteer

A **gazetteer** is a geographical dictionary full of information about places and arranged in alphabetical order by place-names. The information is usually very condensed, which means that much of it is in a kind of 'code'. To get the most out of a gazetteer, we need to know what the symbols mean. Here is the key to a gazetteer of hotels and garages in Britain:

☎	telephone	*unless stated, the name of the exchange is the same as the placename; at hotels the number is usually for reception only*
☏	night telephone	
D	district	
Ec	early closing	
ex	except	
fy	ferry	
Map	figures and letters which follow give the service atlas page number and the national grid reference	
Md	market day	

Garage entries

†	details not confirmed
⅄	garage classification
⚑	Free Breakdown Service classification; service normally available 24 hours every day, unless otherwise shown
🛵	motor-cycle specialist classification
⚑	Free Breakdown Service available Monday–Friday during normal working hours, unless otherwise stated
🛵	motor-cycle and/or scooter repairs undertaken
⚙	approved vehicle testing station at time of going to press; it is advisable to confirm by telephone

Mn	service until midnight
R	repairs and servicing available *outside* normal working hours until time shown
Vau etc	abbreviations for franchises held by garages

Hotel entries

★	hotel classification
☆	hotel classification
⊕	approved hotel
⚨	country-house hotel
◎	mainly grill-type meals
C	closed for two months or more within a year
CC	closed for less than two months at any one time
RS	restricted services operate for a period
U	unlicensed
rm	number of bedrooms
⛴🛁	private bathroom/shower with own toilet
A	annexe (followed by number of rooms)
⊗	no dogs
P	parking on hotel premises (number of cars usually stated)
ℙ	no parking available on hotel premises
nc	no children eg nc4 = no children under 4 years of age

Look at the section from the gazetteer on sheet 28.2 and then answer the questions below:

1 The number after each place-name shows its population.

(*a*) Which is the largest place in the gazetteer?

(*b*) Which is the smallest place?

2 In which counties are these places? (Write the county names in full.)

(*a*) Chartham

(*b*) Chalford

(*c*) Chadlington

(*d*) Charnock Richard

(*e*) Chandler's Ford

112 **Cawston** contd – **Chelmsford**   *England*

Fakennam 18 *London125 Norwich12*
↖M *Marsham* Norwich Rd ☎349 ♣
CAYTHORPE 1,038 Lincs Map25SK94 Grantham9
Lincoln15 London119 Newark12
†**↖M** *Caythorpe Mtrs* 7 Old Lincoln Rd ☎Loveden72386
R20.00 ♣ Sko
CHADLINGTON 717 Oxon Map17SP32 *London74*
Chipping Norton4 *Oxford18*
★**Chadlington House** ☎437 CC 10rm(2⇔M) 23P B&B(b)
CHADWELL HEATH Gt London Map19TQ48
Dartford Tunnel 13 Edmonton11 Ilford5 *London14* Romford2
↖↖↖ *Goodmayes Mtrs Ltd* Clyde Works, Grove Rd
☎01-599 0111 **↖D** Ren Jen Lad
CHAGFORD 1,250 Devon Map6SX78 EcWed *Exeter20*
London192 Moretonhampstead5 Okehampton11
★★★**⛛♨ Great Tree** Sandy Park (2m N on A382) ☎2491
15⇔M 25P
★★★**⛛♨ Mill End** Sandy Park (2m N on A382) ☎2282 RS
18rm(11⇔M) 20P B&B(c)
★★**Greenacres** ☎3471 12rm(4⇔M) 16P nc6 B&B(b)
★★**Moor Park** Lower St ☎2202 18rm(4⇔M) 40P B&B(c)
★★**Three Crowns** ☎3444 10rm(2⇔M) 6P B&B(b)(c)
★♨**Easton Court** Easton Cross (1½m NE A382) ☎3469
8rm(5⇔M) 10P nc12 B&B(b)(c)
CHALE Isle of Wight 537 Map61SZ47 EcThu *London(Fy)91*
Newport10 Hyde17 Ventnor7
↖M *Chale S/Sta* ☎Niton730466 R20.00 ♣
CHALFORD 2,928 Glos MapSO80 *London105*
Cirencester10 Stroud4 Swindon24
★★**Springfield House** (on A419) ☎Brimscombe3555
7rm(5⇔M) 30P B&B(c)
CHANDLER'S FORD 7,200 Hants Map9SU41 EcWed
Eastleigh2 *London71* Romsey4 *Southampton6* Winchester7
↖↖↖ *Hendy Lennox* Hendyford House, Bournemouth Rd
☎66388 ☎Romsey514093 **↖D**20.00 ♣ Frd
↖M *Oakmount S/Sta* Oakmount Rd ☎4298
☎Southampton27434 R20.00 ♣

CHANNEL ISLANDS Details follow England
CHAPEL CLEEVE Somerset Map6ST04 *London179*
Bridgwater22 Minehead7
★★★**Chapel Cleeve Manor** ☎Washford202 13rm(11⇔M)
150P nc5 B&B(c)(d)
CHARD 9,020 Somerset Map7ST30 EcWed MdSat
Exeter30 Ilminster5 *London142 Taunton16* Yeovil17
★★**George** Fore St ☎3413 21rm(3⇔M) 100P B&B(b)
↖↖↖ *Kay Hartnoll Mtrs* Furnham Rd ☎2821 ♣ Sab
↖ *Premier Mtrs* Crewkerne Rd ☎3146 **↖D**21.00
CHARLBURY 2,259 Oxon Map17SP31 Banbury15
Chipping Norton6 *London71 Oxford15*
★★**Bell** Church St ☎278 14rm(6⇔M) ♨ 30P nc5
CHARLTONS Cleveland Map4NZ61 Guisborough3
London251 Middlesbrough12 Whitby19
↖M *Birk Brow S/Sta* ☎Guisborough33009 ☎Skelton
50013
CHARMOUTH 1,017 Dorset Map7SU39 EcThu Bridport7
Dorchester22 *London145* Lyme Regis3
★★**Charmouth House** ☎60319 C 12rm(2⇔M) ♨ 25P
B&B(b)(c)
★★**Fernhill** ☎60492 C 15rm(6⇔M) 50P B&B(b)(c)
★★**Queen's Armes** The Street ☎60339 C 14rm(3⇔M)
15P B&B(b)(c)
★**Sea Horse** Higher Sea Ln ☎60414 C 10rm A6rm 17P
B&B(a)(b)
†**↖↖↖** *Charmouth Mtrs* The Street ☎60308 **↖D** ♣ Frd
CHARNOCK RICHARD 1,684 Lancs Map32SD57
EcWed *London209* Chorley3 Wigan8 *Preston10*
★★★★**♨ TraveLodge** Mill Ln ☎Coppull791746 THF
108⇔M 120P B&B(c)
↖M *Charnock Richard Services* (J A Smith) ☎Coppull
791031 R24hrs
↖M *Preston Road* ☎Coppull791364 R21.00
CHARTHAM 3,970 Kent Map11TR15 EcWed Ashford11
Canterbury4 *London62 Maidstone25*
↖↖↖ *E K V Ltd* Ashford Rd ☎Great Stour331 **↖D** ♣ Vau Opl
CHATHAM 59,550 Kent Map11TQ76 EcWed
Canterbury30 *London32 Maidstone8* Rochester1
↖↖↖ *Dutton Forshaw* 20 Medway St ☎Medway41122
↖D24hrs ♣ BL

---

3 Give the map references for these places:

(a) Charmouth ☐

(c) Caythorpe ☐

(b) Chatham ☐

(d) Charltons ☐

4 In which places can you find 3-star hotels?

☐

5 Which day is early closing day in:

(a) Chard? ☐

(c) Charmouth? ☐

(b) Chagford? ☐

(d) Chartham? ☐

6 In which place is a market held, and on which day?

☐   ☐

7 Find the distances in miles between:

(a) Chapel Cleeve and Minehead ☐

(c) Charmouth and London ☐

(b) Chagford and Exeter ☐

(d) Canterbury and Chartham ☐

8 Give the full telephone numbers of these hotels:

(a) Chadlington House Hotel

(b) Charmouth House Hotel

(c) Easton Court Hotel

(d) Bell Hotel

(e) Springfield House Hotel

9 Use the key on sheet 28.1 to answer these questions about some of the hotels listed:

(a) How many rooms at the Chadlington House Hotel have their own bathroom?

(b) How many cars can park at the Queen's Armes Hotel?

(c) How many rooms are there in the George Hotel?

(d) Which hotel will not accept children under 6 years of age?

(e) Which hotels are country houses?

(f) In which county are they all found?

(g) Which hotels have a 'no dogs' rule?

(h) Which hotel has an annexe?

(i) Which two places listed have the most hotels? Why do you think this is?

10 (a) Which places have the most well-equipped garages?

(b) At what time of day do Premier Motors stop their Free Breakdown Service?

(c) Which garage is a Renault specialist?

(d) For which garages are details not yet confirmed? Why could this be?

Motorway route planner

To make planning motorway journeys easier, organisations like the AA publish motorway route planners. These are not maps, but a guide which show the other roads which join the motorway and the distances between junctions and service areas.

Here is the key to the AA's motorway route planners and part of the M1 London to Milton Keynes route plan:

KEY

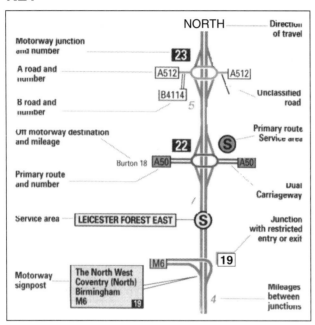

M1 London - Milton Keynes

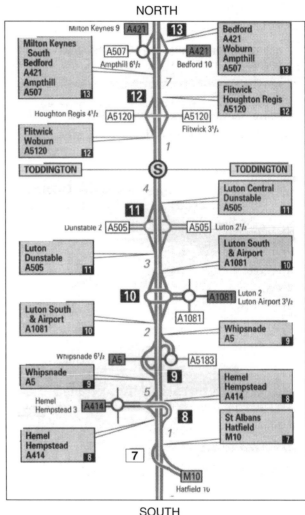

Use the information on the M1 route plan and the key to answer these questions:

1 The M1 motorway is drawn as a [_____] line. It is shown with north at

the [_____] of the route plan and south at the [_____]

2 Which motorway junctions are shown on this part of the route plan?

[_____]

3 What is the distance in miles between these junctions?

(a) 7 and 8 [   ]

(d) 10 and 11 [   ]

(b) 8 and 9 [   ]

(e) 11 and 12 [   ]

(c) 9 and 10 [   ]

(f) 12 and 13 [   ]

4 A slow-moving lorry joins the motorway at Junction 13.
It travels south at 30 mph and leaves the motorway at Junction 7.
How long does it take to travel between Junctions 13 and 7? [   ]

5 You are travelling north on the M1. You leave the motorway at Junction 11
and travel east.

(a) Which A road do you join? [   ]

(b) Which town do you come to? [   ]

(c) How far off the motorway is the town? [   ]

6 You live in Bedford and are setting off to Luton Airport.

(a) Which A road do you travel on to reach the M1? [   ]

(b) At which Junction do you join the M1? [   ]

(c) How far south do you have to travel on the
M1 before you reach the Luton Airport Junction? [   ]

(d) At which Junction do you leave the M1? [   ]

(e) What is your total journey distance from Bedford to Luton Airport? [   ]

7 You are travelling from Hatfield to Milton Keynes via the M1.

(a) At which Junction do you join the M1? [   ]

(b) How far have you travelled before you reach the motorway? [   ]

(c) You decide to stop at the Services area on
this stretch of the M1. Which Services area is it? [   ]

(d) How far have you travelled since you began your journey? [   ]

(e) You have travelled at an average of 50 mph.
How long has it taken you to reach the Services area? [   ]

Planning a road journey

30

You will need a copy of the *AA Handbook* and a gazetteer.

First of all, find the map showing the area around Gloucester.

Using the information on the map, in the other sections of the handbook and in the gazetteer, make a diary and route plan to show this weekend excursion to the Cotswolds. Include **every detail** – road numbers, place names, telephone numbers, hotel names, garages, etc:

> Your family live in Oxford and you all decide to spend the weekend in Gloucestershire. You leave Oxford on Friday evening at 1830, taking the A40 westward. After travelling for half an hour at an average speed of 44 mph, you turn south on the next 'A' road and drive for a further nine miles before stopping to have some crisps at the local pub in the town.
>
> You then turn west on to the A417 and travel for thirteen miles. You stop there for the night, staying in the 3-star hotel.
>
> On Saturday morning you set off on the A429, travelling north. After ten miles you stop off to look around the village.
>
> You continue along the A429 and stop at the next village for lunch, which you eat at the two-star pub and hotel.
>
> Your journey continues along the A429 until you reach the next town, where you turn on to the A424, heading north. After travelling for 15 minutes at 40 mph you stop for a look around the village. You spend the rest of the afternoon there, and have tea at the hotel on The Green. You decide to book in there for Saturday night.
>
> On Sunday morning you set off south along the A46, turning left along the 'B' road at the first road junction. You stop at the second place marked on the map and have coffee at the hotel in The Square. When mum tries to start the car, she finds the electrics have failed, so she calls the AA centre in Gloucester. They can't fix the car on the spot, so they call the garage in Chipping Norton. The car is towed there and it takes until 3 o'clock to repair it.
>
> From there you travel back to Oxford along the shortest route.

Present your diary and route plan in an interesting way. Here is one idea for the basic route plan:

From	Road used	To	Distance (miles)	Hotel names	Garages/ Service centres
1. Oxford	A40				
2.					
3.					

Here are the different ways you can travel by air from Britain to the People's Republic of Polygonia:

Airline	Airport	Day	Flight No.	Stopover at
British Airways	Heathrow	M	BA936	Munich
Air India	Heathrow		AI740	—
Lufthansa	Gatwick		DL613	Bahrain
KLM	Manchester	T	NK824	Rome
Aeroflot	Heathrow		CC142	Moscow
British Airways	Luton	W	BA961	Frankfurt
Lufthansa	Gatwick		DL745	Bahrain
KLM	Luton		NK887	Zurich
Qantas	Heathrow	Th	QA039	Bahrain
Air India	Heathrow		AI788	—
British Airways	Heathrow	F	BA979	Munich
Aeroflot	Gatwick		CC202	Moscow
KLM	Manchester		NK900	Rome

1 How many flights a week do these airlines make to Polygonia?

(a) KLM _____   (b) British Airways _____   (c) Aeroflot _____

2 On which days of the week do Lufthansa operate their service to Polygonia? _____

3 On which day are there fewest flights? _____

4 Which airports do these airlines use?

(a) KLM _____

(b) Air India _____

5 Which airlines use stopovers in these places?

(a) Frankfurt _____   (b) Rome _____

6 Which airline flies non-stop to Polygonia? _____

7 On which days do these flights operate?

(a) DL 745 _____   (c) AI 740 _____

(b) CC 202 _____

8 From which airports do these flights operate?

(a) NK 900 _____   (b) QA 039 _____

It helps to know what the weather's going to be like today. You can watch the **weather forecast** on TV which will tell you what weather to expect over the next 24 hours. Newspapers also carry a **weather map** and other information, to help you plan ahead. Here is part of one set of weather information from a daily newspaper:

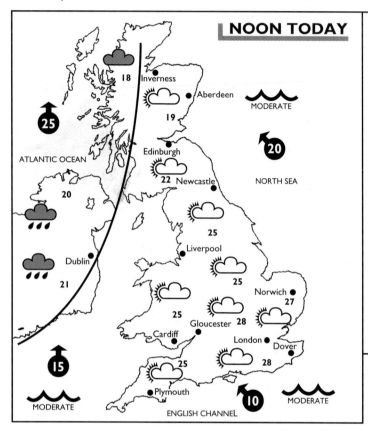

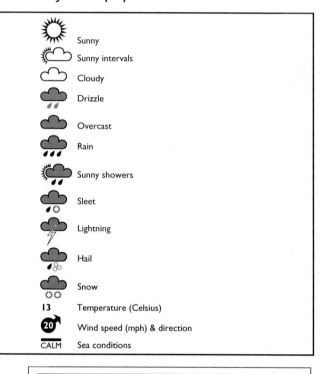

Symbols key:
- Sunny
- Sunny intervals
- Cloudy
- Drizzle
- Overcast
- Rain
- Sunny showers
- Sleet
- Lightning
- Hail
- Snow
- 13 Temperature (Celsius)
- 20 Wind speed (mph) & direction
- CALM Sea conditions

FORECAST

■ **General:** There may be isolated showers near the east coast of England at first but these will soon die out. Most of England and Wales will then be dry and bright.

There will be some sunshine and the South East will be hot and sultry with thundery weather developing in the evening.

Northern Ireland and western Scotland will be cloudy with outbreaks of rain, some perhaps on the heavy side. Eastern Scotland will be mainly dry with bright or sunny spells.

1 London, SE England, E Anglia, Central S England, E Midlands, Channel Isles: Hot and sultry. Thunderstorms developing in the evening. Wind southeast light. Max 28C (82F).

2 E, Central N, NE England, Borders: Early showers then dry with sunny spells. Thundery overnight.

Wind southeast light to moderate. Max 26C (79F).

3 W Midlands, SW, NW England, Wales: Mainly dry with sunny spells, but showers in east overnight. Wind southerly light to moderate. Max 25C (77F).

4 Lake District, Isle of Man, SW Scotland, Glasgow, Central Highlands: Mainly dry, bright spells. Wind southerly moderate. Max 22C (72F).

5 Edinburgh & Dundee, Aberdeen, Moray Firth, NE Scotland, Orkney, Shetland: Dry, bright or sunny spells. Wind southeast moderate to fresh. Max 21C (70F).

6 Argyll, NW Scotland, N Ireland: Cloudy with rain, some perhaps heavy. Wind south moderate to fresh. Max 19C (66F).

■ **Outlook:** Rain spreading across Scotland, W England and Wales, clearing the east on Monday.

AROUND BRITAIN

24 hrs to 6pm: t = thunder; d = drizzle; ds = dust storm; fg = fog; s = sun; sl = sleet; sn = snow; f = fair c = cloud; r = rain; h = hail; du = dull; g = gale; sh = shower; b = bright;

	Sunshine (hours)	Rainfall (inches)	Max. temp °C	Max. temp °F	Weather conditions
Aberdeen	10.1	-	23	73	s
Anglesey	10.4	-	21	70	s
Aspatria	9.2	-	19	66	s
Aviemore	7.6	-	19	66	b
Belfast	7.5	-	19	66	b
Birmingham	7.1	0.04	22	72	s
Bognor R.	4.7	0.06	24	75	b
Bournem'th	7.0	0.03	25	77	s
Bristol	10.0	-	23	73	s
Buxton	7.0	-	20	68	b
Cardiff	11.7	0.11	20	68	s
Clacton	5.2	0.31	21	70	r
Cleethorpes	-	0.61	17	63	r
Cromer	1.2	0.83	18	64	r
Doncaster	2.7	0.28	21	70	r
Dunbar	7.1	-	20	68	b
Eastbourne	5.6	0.59	22	72	b
Edinburgh	10.5	-	21	70	s
Eskdalemuir	8.2	-	18	64	s
Exmouth	11.1	0.01	21	70	s
Fishguard	13.8	-	17	63	s
Folkestone	7.9	0.57	24	75	b
Glasgow	6.4	-	19	66	b
Guernsey	9.2	0.02	20	68	s
Hastings	6.8	0.66	23	73	s
Hayling I.	4.6	0.01	23	73	b
Herne Bay	4.6	0.40	21	70	b
Hove	5.8	0.28	24	75	c
Hunstanton	-	0.65	17	63	r

Look at the *weather map* and its key on sheet 32.1.

1 What are the weather conditions over:

(a) England and Wales? _____

(b) Ireland? _____

(c) North-West Scotland? _____

2 What is the wind direction (where the wind is coming *from*) and wind speed over the:

	Direction	Speed (mph)
(a) English Channel?		
(b) Atlantic Ocean?		
(c) North Sea?		

3 What is the temperature going to be in these places?
(Look at the nearest temperature reading).

°C   °C

(a) London _____   (d) Norwich _____

(b) Dublin _____   (e) Plymouth _____

(c) Inverness _____   (f) Newcastle _____

4 On the day shown on the map, the weather in Ireland is going to be

_____ and _____ .

5 What information on the map tells you that it is summer?

_____

Look at the *Forecast* panel.

6 Most of England and Wales will be _____ and _____ .

7 Which two areas will be cloudy with outbreaks of rain?

_____   _____

Number

8 Which area will have a *South moderate to fresh* wind? _____

If it's easier, write the _number_ of each weather region – look at the Forecast panel

9 Which area of Britain will have the:

Number

(a) highest temperature? [ ]

Number

(b) lowest temperature? [ ]

10 Which areas will have thunder overnight? [ ]

11 (a) Is the weather in England going to get better or worse over the next few days? [ ]

(b) Which section of the Forecast tells you? [ ]

Look at the _Around Britain_ panel. This records weather conditions the day before the newspaper was printed.

12 Which place had the:

(a) longest hours of sunshine? [ ]

(b) most rain? [ ]

(c) highest temperature? [ ]

13 What were the weather conditions in:

(a) Exmouth? [ ]

(c) Aviemore? [ ]

(b) Hunstanton? [ ]

(d) Hove? [ ]

14 How many more hours of sunshine did:

(a) Bristol have than Hastings? [ ]

(b) Edinburgh have than Aberdeen? [ ]

(c) Guernsey have than Hove? [ ]

15 What was the difference in temperature between:

°C   °F

(a) Bournemouth and Hunstanton? [ ]   [ ]

(b) Folkestone and Glasgow? [ ]   [ ]

(c) Cleethorpes and Hastings? [ ]   [ ]

Deciding where to go on holiday - and whether you can afford it - is a difficult business. There are so many holiday companies offering all sorts of complicated 'package holidays' (which means the price you pay includes your travel and accommodation), and very often the advertised price does not show 'extras' and surcharges.

The Travel Club, based at Station Road, Upminster, Essex RM14 2TT (01708 225000), have been organising package holidays since 1936, and their pricing system is simpler than most!

This piece of work is based on a two-week holiday in The Travel Club's Troulakis studios and apartments in Aghia Marina on the island of Crete.

Read the information on sheet 33.2 to find out about the Troulakis apartments and how much a holiday there will cost.

1 How far away from the village of Aghia Marina are the Troulakis apartments?

2 What is the name of the other village nearby?

3 What are the first names of the owners of the apartments?

4 What is their surname?

5 How far away is Hania?

6 Where is the Travel Club office?

7 A *kitchenette* is not a separate room. It's a corner of another room with fridge, cooker, sink and cupboards.

(*a*) How many rooms does each studio have?

What are they?

(*b*) How many rooms does each one bedroom apartment have?

What are they?

(*c*) How many rooms does each two bedroom apartment have?

What are they?

TROULAKIS STUDIOS AND APARTMENTS

These excellent studios, one and two bedroom apartments are exclusive to Travel Club clients, who are always made very welcome by the owners Giorgos, Tula, Stratis and Anna. They are set on a long wide beach of coarse sand 500 metres from the villages of Aghia Marina and Platanias. There are several shops, mini-markets, tavernas and bars within easy walking distance and the local bus service will take you into Hania, 10 kms away. The Travel Club office is directly opposite and in addition to answering your questions on what to do and where to go it also offers a money changing facility.

In the gardens between the apartments and the beach there is a snack bar run by the Troulakis family and this serves drinks, snacks and ice creams. Sun loungers and sun umbrellas can be hired on the beach, where watersports are also available.

The studios have kitchenette with fridge and electric hob, bathroom with shower and wc, lounge/bedroom with two divans and balcony with side sea view.

The apartments have kitchenette and bathroom as above, lounge/dining room with one extra bed, balcony or terrace with front or side sea view and either one twin bedded room or one twin and one double bedded room.

Official rating: A Class

REFERENCE

TR/SO Studio (based on **two** adults)

TR/A1 One bedroom apartment (based on **two** adults)

TR/A2 Two bedroom apartment (based on **three** adults)

One extra bed is available in the above apartments. Reduction per each additional adult or supplement per each missing adult.

Apr 11 - June 26:	£70 per week
Jun 27 - Sep 11:	£90 per week
Sep 12 - Oct 9:	£85 per week

TROULAKIS
PRICES IN £'S PER PERSON

Reference	TR/A2 two bedroom apartment		TR/A1 one bedroom apartment		TR/SO studio	
Departing	1wk	**2wk**	1wk	**2wk**	1wk	**2wk**
Apr 11,18	298	**364**	308	**388**	288	**348**
Apr 25	284	**348**	298	**374**	278	**334**
May 2	288	**354**	298	**378**	284	**338**
May 9	298	**378**	314	**398**	298	**364**
May 16	324	**398**	338	**428**	318	**384**
May 23	354	**424**	368	**454**	344	**408**
May 30	364	**414**	378	**444**	358	**398**
Jun 6	338	**414**	354	**444**	334	**398**
Jun 13	338	**414**	354	**444**	334	**398**
Jun 20	338	**424**	354	**454**	334	**408**
Jun 27	348	**434**	364	**464**	338	**414**
Jul 4,11	348	**434**	364	**464**	338	**414**
Jul 18	348	**444**	364	**478**	338	**424**
Jul 25	358	**448**	378	**488**	348	**434**
Aug 1	358	**448**	378	**488**	348	**434**
Aug 8	358	**448**	378	**488**	348	**434**
Aug 15	358	**448**	378	**488**	348	**434**
Aug 22	358	**444**	378	**484**	348	**428**
Aug 29	354	**438**	368	**474**	344	**424**
Sep 5	354	**438**	368	**468**	344	**418**
Sep 12	348	**434**	364	**464**	338	**414**
Sep 19	334	**418**	354	**454**	328	**398**
Sep 26	334	**408**	354	**438**	328	**394**
Oct 3	308		324		298	

Day flights on **TUESDAYS** to HANIA on *special services* from GATWICK. See page 49 for details of flight timings and car hire available from £138 per week.

8 How many beds are there in each:

(a) studio? ☐

(b) one bedroom apartment? ☐

(c) two bedroom apartment? ☐

9 Each size of studio and apartment is given a reference code.
What do these codes stand for?

(a) TR/SO ☐

(b) TR/A1 ☐

(c) TR/A2 ☐

10 Look at the price list and write down how much these holidays would cost per person:

(a) 2 weeks in a studio from 6 June ☐

(b) 2 weeks in a two bedroom apartment from 25 April ☐

(c) 2 weeks in a one bedroom apartment from 29 August ☐

(d) 1 week in a two bedroom apartment from 16 May ☐

(e) 1 week in a studio from 25 July ☐

11 (a) On which day of the week would you fly out to Crete? ☐

(b) What is the name of the airport in Crete? ☐

(c) From which UK airport does your journey begin? ☐

(d) The flight leaves Gatwick at 0830 and takes 4 hours. Travel time from Hania
to the Troulakis apartments is 35 minutes. What is the earliest time you could get
to the apartments (in UK time)?

☐

12 Most people go on holiday with friends or their family. How much would a holiday in the Troulakis studios and apartments cost these groups?

DON'T FORGET – THE PRICES ON THE LIST ARE PER PERSON!

Group	Accommodation	Length of holiday	Departing	Total cost
2 adults	studio	2 weeks	15 August	
2 adults	one bedroom apartment	1 week	5 September	
3 adults	two bedroom apartment	2 weeks	20 June	

If you take **more** than the number of adults on which the studio or apartment's price is based, The Travel Club give you a **reduction** on your total price. If you take **less** than the number of adults on which the price is based, you have to pay a supplement (extra charge). The information on sheet 33.2 tells you that the price per person for:

> TR/S0 is based on two adults
> TR/A1 is based on two adults
> TR/A2 is based on three adults

Look at the information on sheet 33.2 to see how much the reduction (or supplement) is. It depends on when you go!

Here are two examples:

> If 3 adults want to stay in a one bedroom apartment (TR/A1) for two weeks from 18 July, the total cost works out like this:
>
> 3 x £478 cost per person ═ £1,434
>
> **Less** a reduction of
> £90 per week for 1 extra adult
> (because the price for TR/A1
> is based on only **two** adults):
>
> 2 weeks x £90 per week ═ £180
> ─────────
> Actual cost of holiday £1,254

If 2 adults want to stay in a two bedroom apartment (TR/A2)
for two weeks from 30 May, the total cost works out like this:

2 x £414 cost per person	=	£828
Plus a supplement of £70 per week for the 1 missing adult *(because the price for TR/A2 is based on **three** adults):*		
2 weeks x £70 per week	=	£140
Actual cost of holiday		£968

13 How much would these holidays cost, taking into account any supplements or reductions? Show your working out in the boxes:

(a) One adult staying in a studio for 2 weeks from 19 September:

(c) Four adults staying in a two bedroom apartment for 1 week from 2 May:

(b) Three adults staying in a one bedroom apartment for 2 weeks from 13 June:

(d) One adult staying in in a one bedroom apartment for 2 weeks from 22 August:

When you go abroad for a holiday, you need to know what **currency** (money) is used in the country you are going to. You also need to know what the **exchange rate** is at the time you go - this means how much of the local currency you can buy for each UK pound (*£ sterling*). Look at this popular holiday destination, the currency used and the exchange rate:

Country	Currency	Exchange rate for each £
Barbados	Barbados dollar ($)	3.1678

That means that for each £ you get 3.1678 Barbados dollars: in other words, there are $3.1678 for every UK £.

You can work out the value of each Barbados $ by dividing one pound (£1) by the exchange rate (3.1678):

$$£1 ÷ 3.1678 = £0.3156764 . . .$$

That means that each Barbados dollar is worth **£0.32** or **32p**
(notice that the number has been rounded up to the nearest penny).

Look at this table of some other holiday destinations and their currency exchange rates:

Country	Currency	Exchange rate
Antigua	East Caribbean $	4.2525
Australia	Australian $	2.0789
Austria	Schilling	16.8276
Azores	Portuguese Escudo	246.777
Bahamas	Bahama $	1.5649
Balearic Isles	Spanish Peseta	207.476
Barbados	Barbados $	3.1678
Canada	Canadian $	2.1947
Canary Islands	Spanish Peseta	207.476
Cayman Islands	Cayman Island $	1.3044
China	Yuan	13.2049
Cuba	Cuban Peso	1.5649
Cyprus	Cyprus £	0.7415
Denmark	Danish Krone	9.4216
Dominica	East Caribbean $	4.2525
Egypt	Egyptian £	5.3563
Finland	Markka	7.3917
France	Franc	8.2875
Gambia	Dalasi	15.3956
Greece	Drachma	372.747
Iceland	Icelandic Krona	105.840
India	Indian Rupee	49.1011
Ireland	Punt	1.0108
Israel	Shekel	4.7178

Country	Currency	Exchange rate
Jamaica	Jamaican $	50.9985
Malaysia	Ringgit	3.9959
Malta	Maltese Lira	0.5734
Mauritius	Mauritius Rupee	28.0901
Morocco	Dirham	13.8474
New Zealand	New Zealand $	2.4576
Pakistan	Pakistan Rupee	48.2429
Philippines	Peso	38.8083
Portugal	Escudo	246.777
Russia	Rouble	6463.00
Seychelles	Rupee	7.7411
Singapore	$	2.2816
South Africa	Rand	6.3533
Spain	Peseta	207.476
Sri Lanka	Rupee	78.0861
Switzerland	Franc	2.0188
Thailand	Baht	39.2152
Trinidad	$	8.9381
Tunisia	Dinar	1.5435
Turkey	Lira	63611.2
United States	US $	1.5649
Virgin Islands	US $	1.5649

1 Name the currency and exchange rate shown for these countries:

(*a*) Morocco

(*b*) Greece

(*c*) Spain

(*d*) United States

(*e*) France

(*f*) Mauritius

2 Which countries use these currencies?

(*a*) Punt

(*b*) Baht

(*c*) Schilling

(*d*) Markka

(*e*) Dinar

(*f*) Rouble

3 Which two countries have an exchange rate less than 1?
(Which means their unit of currency is worth more than £1.)

4 Which currency will you get most of for £1?

(Look for the highest figure!)

5 Which country has the closest exchange rate to the £?

(Look for the exchange rate closest to 1.)

6 If I want to change £50 into local currency, how much will I get in these countries?
(Multiply!)

	Currency	How much I get for £50
(*a*) China		
(*b*) Sri Lanka		
(*c*) Israel		
(*d*) United States		
(*e*) Malta		

7 Remember how to work out the value of each unit of currency in pounds?
(Look back at sheet 34.1). Work out what one of each of these is worth in pounds.
Give your answer to the nearest penny, rounded up or down:

(a) Dirham

(b) Rand

(c) Dalasi

(d) Peseta

(e) Egyptian £

(f) Ringgit

8 Work out what these items cost in UK pounds (divide the price by the exchange rate).
Give your answer to the nearest penny.

(a)

(b)

(c)

(d)

(e)

(f)

(g)

(h)

(i)

(j)

800 Schillings

65 Dalasi

1 Maltese Lira

1,000 Escudos

500 Indian Rupees

50 Shekels

400 Baht

5 Dinars

40 Dirhams

COFFEE 250 Pesetas

When people want to sell or buy something 'second hand' they often use the **classified** advertisements section of newspapers or magazines. There you will find 'small ads' which are often just a few lines of print and which offer all sorts of items for sale.

Look at this batch of small ads:

CLASSIFIED

COFFEE TABLE, oak veneer, vgc, £60 ono. 0181 925 3524

SHARP VLC690 CAMCORDER, battery, charger, light, used once. Accept £500. 0171 225 8209

MOUNTAIN BIKE, 21 gears, Apollo frame, Shimano components, pump and helmet, £180 ono. 0181 375 8099

JVC PC70 PORTABLE STEREO, detachable speakers, auto reverse. £45 ono. 0171 503 7764

TOYOTA KS 950 KNITTING MACHINE complete with video, magazines and stand. £450. 0181 435 8122 eves.

AEG 8209 CYLINDER VACUUM CLEANER, as new, microfilter, 1500 watt motor, energy saver setting. Offers over £150. 0171 886 5092

TUNTURI ROWING MACHINE model 203, excellent condition, hardly used. £100. 0171 556 6273

GOLF CLUBS, 9 irons, graphite sandwich, as new. £150. 01708 522 1080

METRO CITY X 1.0, 1989, silver, 52,000 miles, full service history, 6 months tax, MoT November. £2,675. 0181 664 8993

LEATHER JACKET, biker style, size 42, excellent condition, £90. 01280 73924

THREE-PIECE SUITE, 3 seater couch, brown velvet, hardly used. Excellent value. £250. 0171 203 5881

SATELLITE SYSTEM, complete, decoder, scart sockets, Astra 1D compatible, 60 cm black mesh dish, year's guarantee. £225 ono. Will deliver. 0181 765 2093

1 Use the classified page from your local newspaper to help you find out what these abbreviations mean:

(a) vgc

(b) ono

(c) eves

2 Write down the telephone number you would ring if you wanted to use the small ads on sheet 35.1 to buy something to:

(a) sit on

(b) ride

(c) drive

(d) help you keep fit

(e) increase the range of TV channels you can watch

(f) put your cups on

(g) wear

(h) help you keep your house clean

(i) make your own clothes with

(j) play your tapes on

3 Which item could you get delivered to you?

4 Which item is a silver colour?

5 With which item do you get a video and magazines?

6 With which item do you get a year's guarantee?

7 Which item has only been used once?

8 Which two items are sold 'as new'?

9 Which is the cheapest item in this section of the classified ads?

Value Added Tax (VAT) is a tax added on to the price you pay for a very wide range of products and services. This means you pay more when you buy the product or pay for the service. The company which sells you the product or service then pays the VAT it collects to the Government.

The rate of VAT can go up or down, depending on how much the Government needs to raise in tax, but VAT is usually somewhere between 15-20% of the price. It appears at the end of a bill, like this:

INVOICE

AZ CAR SERVICES LTD
VAT Reg No 793 1104 25

Ford Escort M352 ZTT	
Wheel bearing	24.95
4 spark plugs	12.47
1 oil filter	7.75
1 air filter	10.58
1 set brake pads	37.88
Labour	65.00
Total	158.63
VAT @ 17 ½%	27.76
Total this invoice	£186.39

THANK YOU FOR YOUR CUSTOM

This means that your bill from AZ Car Services came to £158.63, but you had to pay an extra £27.76 in VAT. AZ Car Services will then pay the £27.76, together with all the other VAT they collect this month, to HM Customs and Excise, who collect all VAT for the Government.

To work out VAT on a calculator, you use this keystroke sequence:

The amount on which VAT is to be charged	The VAT rate in force at the time	Gives the amount of VAT to be charged
1 5 8 . 6 3 x	1 7 . 5 %	2 7 . 7 6

Use a calculator to work out the amount of VAT which will be charged on these bills (give each answer to the nearest penny):

				VAT
1	£95.36	+	VAT at 17.5%	£
2	£35.42	+	VAT at 17.5%	£
3	£155.24	+	VAT at 8%	£
4	£2432	+	VAT at 15%	£
5	£6495	+	VAT at 17.5%	£

It would be very complicated if you had to add VAT every time you went shopping, so most prices displayed in stores already *include* VAT. Look at this item:

The price of the CD/cassette player is £269.95, which *includes* VAT. To find out how much VAT you are paying, you need to divide the total price by (100% + the VAT rate), then multiply by the VAT rate:

$$\frac{£269.95}{117.5} \quad \times \quad 17.5 \quad = \quad £40.21$$

Calculator keystrokes:

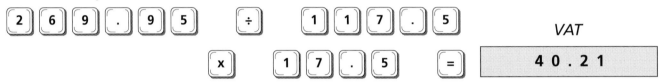

So you will pay £40.21 VAT as part of the price of the CD/cassette player.

Work out the VAT which is included in these prices:

VAT

6 £354.95 (VAT 17.5%)

7 £755.99 (VAT 15%)

8 £244.50 (VAT 18%)

9 £36.95 (VAT 20%)

10 £2599 (VAT 17.5%)

If you want to find out what the **net** price of the item is (that means the price without the VAT), you can use a similar set of keystrokes to find it:

$$\frac{£269.95}{117.5} \quad \times \quad 100 \quad = \quad £229.75$$

Calculator keystrokes:

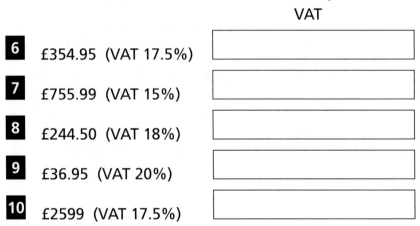

Work out the net price of each of these items (VAT at 17.5%):

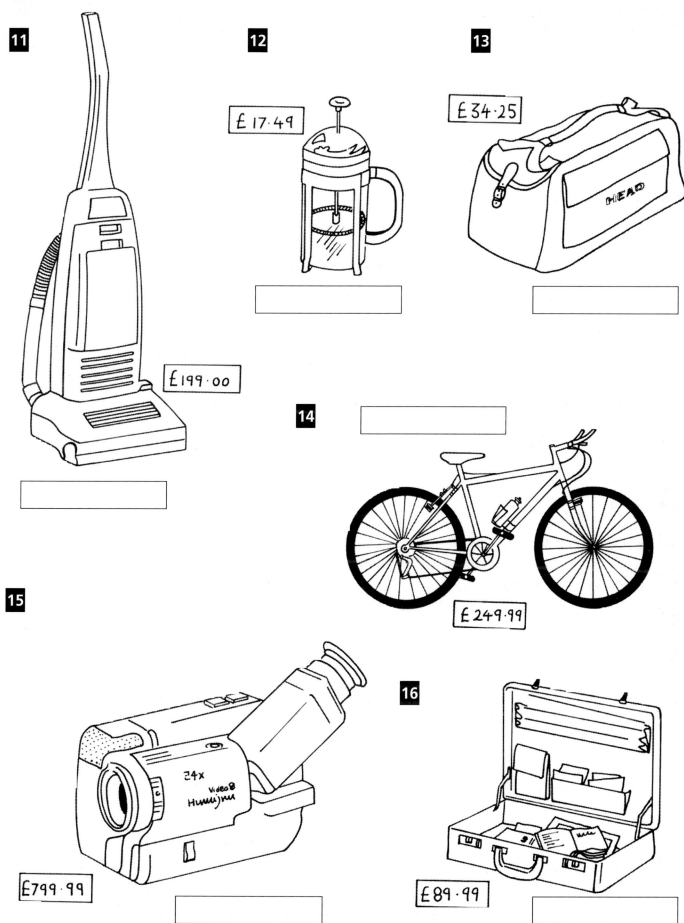

11

£199·00

12

£17·49

13

£34·25

14

£249·99

15

£799·99

16

£89·99

To encourage you to buy their products or services, companies will very often offer you a **discount**. That means they will reduce their price by a certain amount. This happens when a store holds a sale.

SALE NOW ON

MASSIVE REDUCTIONS

Most stores also run 'special offers' all year round, to tempt you into buying the products which have the reduced prices:

SPECIAL OFFER

CAR SHAMPOO HALF PRICE
WAS
~~£8.50~~
NOW
£4.25

5 LITRES OIL
~~£18.50~~
REDUCED TO
£15.99

£5 OFF
CAR WAX
~~£12.95~~
SPECIAL OFFER PRICE
£7.95

For larger items, like cars, dealers will often offer a percentage discount. If a car costs £12,995 and the dealer offers a 15% discount, the actual price you pay will be:

£12,995 **minus** 15% of £12,995

You work out the discount like this on a calculator:

Discount

[1] [2] [9] [9] [5]   [x]   [1] [5] [%]   ⟶   1 9 4 9 . 2 5

You can then subtract the discount from the price of the car to find out the actual or **net** price you will pay:

£12,995.00

- £ 1,949.25
‾‾‾‾‾‾‾‾‾‾‾
£11,045.75

Work out the net prices of each of these cars:

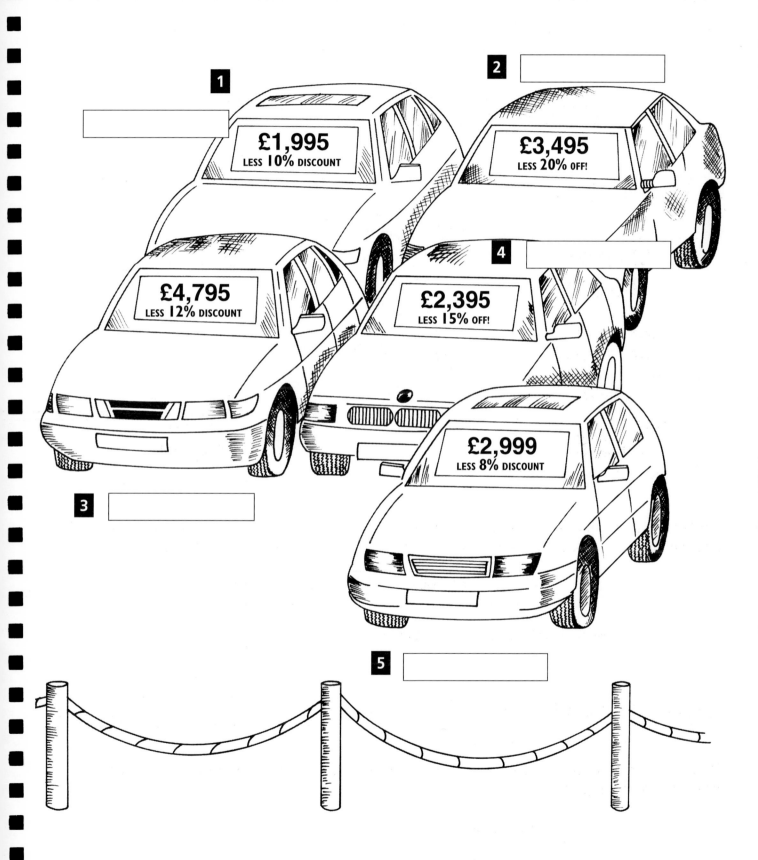

1

£1,995
LESS 10% DISCOUNT

2

£3,495
LESS 20% OFF!

£4,795
LESS 12% DISCOUNT

4

£2,395
LESS 15% OFF!

£2,999
LESS 8% DISCOUNT

3

5

Personal banking: Budget Account

38

If you spend more than you earn, you will find that you cannot pay the bills which are part of everyday life. 'Budgeting' means *planning* how much you need to put aside for the bills you have to pay.

When you first start work, or move into a new home, you have to **estimate** how much your bills will be. When you've paid them, you can check back to see if your estimate was right.

To make things easier, most banks will help you set up a **Budget Account**. This is a **separate** account from the 'current' account your wages are paid into. You use your Budget Account cheque book or payment card to settle the main bills you have to pay. A regular amount is automatically transferred from your current account to your Budget Account to cover the cost of the bills.

Here's how it works:

- You work out the **annual cost** of all your bills over a full twelve months

- You divide the total by twelve to work out the average monthly cost of your bills

- Your bank then transfers that amount each month from your current account to your Budget Account

- As each bill comes in, you pay it from your Budget Account

- Your bank will make a monthly charge on your Budget Account to cover their administration costs. They will also charge interest if your Budget Account becomes 'overdrawn' (if, for example, you pay a bill for £100 when your account only has £20 left in it - during that month you would pay interest on the £80 you had 'borrowed' from the bank).

You earn £250 a week, out of which you have to pay £45 a week in tax and national insurance. These are deducted before you get your wages:

1 Your 'net' pay each week (what you have left after tax and national insurance) is

£ _____

> You pay £120 a week rent for your flat. Your telephone bills will be about £60 a quarter. Water rates will be £290 per year. Your bus travel pass costs £35 a month. Electricity will cost about £4.50 a week. You have to pay Council Tax in ten monthly instalments of £33. You have bought a colour TV and need to pay the annual licence fee (£93). Clothes might work out at about £250 a year and household items might come to £250 a year also. You have taken out life insurance, which will cost you £225 a year, and you have insured the contents of your flat (annual premium £47). The bank charges £2 a month for running your Budget Account.

2 Complete this annual budget planner, showing how you worked out the annual cost of each bill:

		Annual cost (£)
Budget Account charges	£2 per month x 12	24
Rent		
Council Tax		
Electricity		
Telephone		
Water Rates		
Life insurance		
Home Contents insurance		
Monthly travel pass		
TV licence		
Clothes		
Household items		
	Total annual cost:	£

3 What is the average monthly cost of these bills?

4 What is the average weekly cost of these bills?

Your answer to question 1 on sheet 38.2 tells you how much you have left after tax and national insurance are deducted from your wages. If you take away the average weekly cost of your bills from that answer, you will find out how much money you will have left each week for food and 'extras'.

5 (a) How much is left?

(b) How did you work it out?

6 Because you are working well, you get a 4% pay rise.

(a) How much is that per week?

(b) What is the 'net' amount of the pay increase (the amount left if you take off 25% tax/national insurance)?

(c) What is your **annual** net pay increase? (Multiply your answer to (b) by the number of weeks in a year.)

7 You decide to put most of your net pay rise into your Budget Account to go towards a holiday costing £345.

(a) Add the cost of the holiday to the total annual cost of your budget plan (see question 2 on sheet 38.2). What is the new total annual cost?

(b) What is the new amount which the bank needs to transfer each month from your current account to your Budget Account?

Banks send their customers regular **statements**, to show how much money has been put into or taken out of their bank account during the past month. When you get the statement, you can check to see whether the right payments have been made and how much you have left. You will find this information on a bank statement:

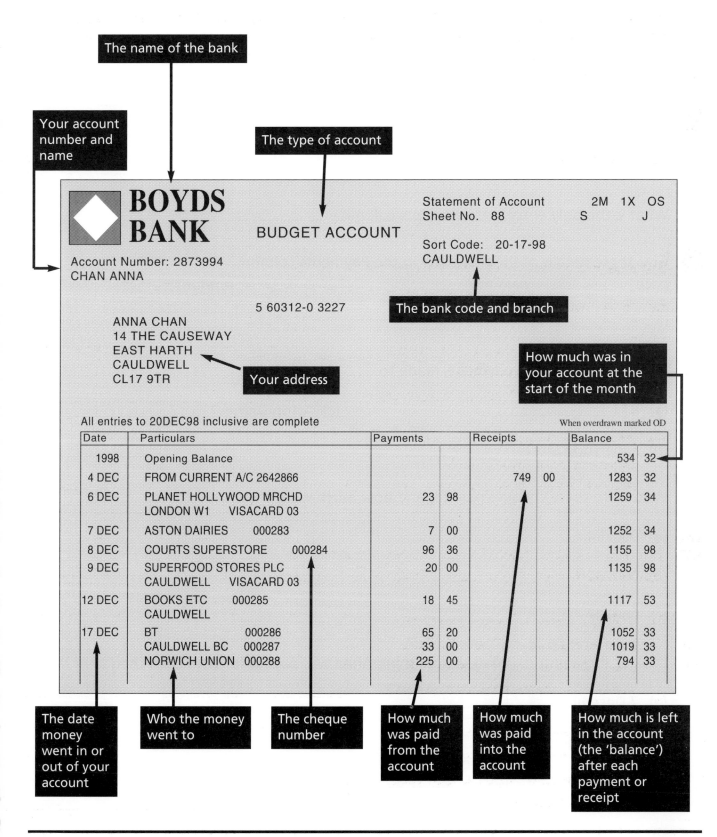

The name of the bank

Your account number and name

The type of account

BOYDS BANK

BUDGET ACCOUNT

Account Number: 2873994
CHAN ANNA

5 60312-0 3227

ANNA CHAN
14 THE CAUSEWAY
EAST HARTH
CAULDWELL
CL17 9TR

Your address

Statement of Account   2M   1X   OS
Sheet No.   88   S   J

Sort Code: 20-17-98
CAULDWELL

The bank code and branch

How much was in your account at the start of the month

All entries to 20DEC98 inclusive are complete   When overdrawn marked OD

Date	Particulars	Payments		Receipts		Balance	
1998	Opening Balance					534	32
4 DEC	FROM CURRENT A/C 2642866			749	00	1283	32
6 DEC	PLANET HOLLYWOOD MRCHD LONDON W1 VISACARD 03	23	98			1259	34
7 DEC	ASTON DAIRIES 000283	7	00			1252	34
8 DEC	COURTS SUPERSTORE 000284	96	36			1155	98
9 DEC	SUPERFOOD STORES PLC CAULDWELL VISACARD 03	20	00			1135	98
12 DEC	BOOKS ETC 000285 CAULDWELL	18	45			1117	53
17 DEC	BT 000286	65	20			1052	33
	CAULDWELL BC 000287	33	00			1019	33
	NORWICH UNION 000288	225	00			794	33

The date money went in or out of your account

Who the money went to

The cheque number

How much was paid from the account

How much was paid into the account

How much is left in the account (the 'balance') after each payment or receipt

1 (a) What is Anna's Budget Account number?

(b) What is her current account number?

2 (a) What is the name of the bank?

(b) What is the bank's Sort Code?

3 What was the Opening Balance in the account at the beginning of December?

4 What was the final balance in the account at the end of business on 17 December?

5 What is the only entry in the **Receipts** column?

6 Give these details of the first entry in the **Payments** column:
date   paid to   amount

7 On which dates were payments made to:

(a) BT?

(c) Aston Dairies?

(b) Superfood Stores?

8 Who were these cheques paid to, and how much were they for?

(a) 000284   £

(b) 000285   £

(c) 000287   £

9 Look at these entries. What do you think Anna was paying for with each cheque or VISA?

(a) 7 December

(b) 9 December

(c) 12 December

Choosing the right car is a difficult decision. The car market is very competitive and car *dealers* (the companies who sell cars direct to the public) try to make the cars they sell sound as attractive as possible. They offer different deals to try to persuade you to buy a car from them, especially **part exchange** (which means they take a certain amount off the price of a new car if you give them your old one) and **discounts** if you pay 'in cash' (in other words, if you pay for the car in one go rather than spreading the cost over several months or years). They also offer **reduced finance** deals, which means you can pay for the car in monthly instalments at a reduced rate of interest: some dealers even offer 0% finance, which means you don't pay any interest at all (you pay a deposit, then the rest of the cost of the car is just divided by the number of months over which you will pay it off).

Look at the advertisements for hatchbacks below and on sheet 40.2 to help you answer the questions on sheets 40.2 and 40.3:

SEEING IS BELIEVING...

FIAT CINQUECENTO
1.2 HATCHBACK
MINIMUM £1,200 PART EXCHANGE
ONLY £7,495 ON THE ROAD
(includes year's road tax)

* 5 Speed gearbox   * sunroof
* alloy wheels   * rear wash/wipe
* colour co-ordinated trim
* 60.1 mpg @ 56mph   * digital radio

Mount Rise Autos (01342) 744818 Station Precinct, Adfield

CRAWFORDS
THE PEUGEOT SPECIALISTS

(01342 711622) The Rise, Adfield
PEUGEOT 106 "PLUS"

* **Quality radio cassette**
* **Analogue clock**
* **Body side mouldings**
* **Remote control door mirrors**
* **57.6 mpg @ 56 mph**
* **Road fund licence**

PART EXCHANGE WELCOME
FREE MOBILE PHONE

Plu **FREE** COMPREHENSIVE INSURANCE
Plu **3** YEARS MANUFACTURERS WARRANTY
Plu **3** YEARS AA COVER
Plu **NO** HIDDEN EXTRAS

£8249 on the road

MINIMUM **£500** PART EXCHANGE FOR YOUR OLD CAR

20% Discount for cash

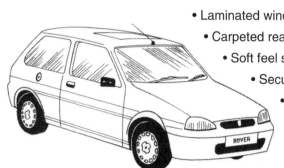

• 3-door Hatchback
• Laminated windscreen
• Carpeted rear parcel shelf
• Soft feel steering wheel
• Security alarm
• Choice of colours
• 6-year anti-corrosion warranty
• 3-year cosmetic/paint warranty
• 61.7 mpg at constant 56mph
• Lively 1.1 engine

Rover 111i

4 YEARS 0% APR Finance

£7,945

Deposit	£45
Balance	£7900
48 months @ £164.58	

AGL MOTORS, (01342) 898611, Station Precinct, Adfield

FREE TANK OF PETROL
(plates, delivery extra)

YES, YOU CAN AFFORD A NEW CAR!

From Super Cars (01342) 877500
Hearst Farm Industrial Estate, Adfield

SAMARA 1.3S

Yes! Available now! Brand new Lada Samara Hatchbacks and Saloons, with the following outstanding features:

• Spoiler • Sunroof • Alloy Wheels • Five Speed Gearbox
• Excellent Fuel Economy • 2 Year/50,000 Miles Warranty
• Internally Adjustable Mirrors • 6 Year Bodywork Warranty
• Heated Rear Window with Wash/Wipe • Stereo Radio Cassette
• 1 Year National Breakdown Membership

£5995 ON THE ROAD

LO-FINANCE AVAILABLE
APR 9.8% OVER 48 MONTHS

£1500 MINIMUM PART EXCHANGE

Yes! That old car you are driving could be worth a small fortune in part exchange for a brand new Samara
Ask for details

---

1 Which cars are being advertised?

Make	Model

2 Which car is the:

(a) most expensive? [ ]   (b) cheapest? [ ]

3 Two dealers have showrooms in the same road. Which dealers are they?

[ ]   [ ]

4 Which dealer is offering:

(a) 3 years' AA cover?

(b) a free tank of petrol?

(c) National Breakdown membership?

(d) £1,200 part exchange?

(e) 0% finance?

5 Which cars have these features?

(a) Security alarm?

(b) Colour co-ordinated trim?

(c) Spoiler?

6 What engine sizes are the:

(a) Lada Samara?

(b) Rover 111i?

(c) Fiat Cinquecento?

A *warranty* is a guarantee. If something goes wrong with the car during the period of the warranty, the dealer will repair it free of charge. An *anti-corrosion* warranty covers the bodywork, but not the engine. A paint warranty covers the paint, but not the engine.

7 What kinds of warranty are offered on the:

(a) Peugeot 106?

(b) Lada Samara?

(c) Rover 111i?

8 Which dealer offers a free mobile phone with the car?

9 (*a*) Why is AGL Motors' 0% finance deal attractive?

(*b*) How much would you pay each month?

(*c*) Over how many years can you pay off the Rover 111i?

10 Work out the net cost of the:

(*a*) Fiat Cinquecento if you part exchange your old car

(*c*) Peugeot 106 if you pay in cash

(*b*) Lada Samara if you part exchange your old car

(*d*) Peugeot 106 if you part exchange your old car

11 What are your five main reasons for choosing one car rather than another?

1

2

3

4

5

Discuss your reasons in a group.

12 Which of the four cars advertised do you think offers the best **value for money** (the most features and best quality for the money you pay)?

Looking for a job

41

Thinking about a job can be a bewildering experience, and lots of people try different kinds of work before they find a job that they really like. There is a great deal of competition for every job advertised and it's very important to make the best impression when you apply.

There are two main ways of applying for a job:

Telephoning
The advertisement will usually give a contact name and a telephone number. The company will interview you over the phone. If they like what they hear, you will be invited to visit their offices for a face-to-face interview. To get past the first stage, you need a good *telephone manner*: you need to be clear, polite, friendly, unflustered - and sound confident!

Writing
The advertisement will usually give a contact name and the company's address, and will sometimes ask for a *letter of application* or a CV (curriculum vitae). A CV is your 'career history' which sets out what jobs you have done, what qualifications you have and what other interests/ activities you are involved in. If you are asked to 'apply in writing', it's a good idea to write an application letter and attach your CV.

On sheets 41.2 and 41.3 you will see two pages from a local newspaper's *Recruitment Fair* section, which show a selection of the jobs advertised this week. Look at the advertisements and then answer these questions:

1 How many job advertisements are there?

2 Each advertisement panel is identified by a letter of the alphabet. Which panels advertise these jobs?

(*a*) car valeters

(*b*) sales assistant

(*c*) car cleaner/driver

(*d*) part time stylist

(*e*) fitness/leisure apprentice

(*f*) trainee kennel help

3 Write down the contact name for these companies/organisations:

(*a*) Aqua Sport Ltd

(*b*) Millbank Service Station

(*c*) Austin Road out of school project

(*d*) Linda Scott's Fitness Club

(*e*) ACR Citroen

recruitment FAIR

A

Kentucky Fried Chicken

FULL TIME/PART TIME
STAFF
REQUIRED URGENTLY

Flexible hours to suit.
Aged 18 years
and over.

Please apply:

The Manager

**Tel: Hilton Mowbray
(01735) 311717**

(Mon-Thurs)

B

AEROBIC FITNESS/LEISURE
APPRENTICE REQUIRED

We are looking for an enthusiastic, smart person with personality. He/she must have a flexible attitude to the varied work within a leading Health & Fitness Club in Hilton Mowbray. Training leading to National Qualifications will be given to the successful applicant.
Telephone Andy Scott (01735) 644444 for more details

LINDA SCOTT'S FITNESS CLUB

C

WE ARE LOOKING FOR SALES SUPERSTARS
£50,000 P.A. (OTE)!

For the 4th year, we as a company have broken all records, to take a massive £60,000,000 Sales. The company's top "Goal Scorers" have earned over £40,000, that's £800 per week, every week. We are talent scouting for new players, male or female. *If you are a car owner and interested in:-*
• A new career • No cold calling • Earn while you learn - then contact us now for a local interview.

**MIKE YOUNG (Team Manager)
FREEPHONE 0800 994286**

A SHEERWATER PLC COMPANY

D

PC HELP DESK SUPPORT
Whatever hours you can offer, we need you NOW!!

Weekends, evenings & days available. Must have IT exp. Dos & Windows. Providing technical support over the telephone.

Excellent telephone manner with the ability to deal with enquiries and complaints.

Could suit Students, returning Mums and early retired.

TEL: (01735) 664455
ACORN PERSONNEL SERVICES
Acorn House, Kingsway, Hilton Mowbray

E

MILLBANK SERVICE STATION
Full time Sales Assistant
required
Six months sales experience preferred but not essential
Contact: Mr Archer on
670232

F

PART TIME KITCHEN ASSISTANT REQUIRED

Mon-Fri Lunchtimes
10.30am to 3.00pm

Must be reliable and have a good sense of humour for our friendly working environment.

**Apply to:
The Manager
André's Bistro
01735 609998**

G

Junior Secretary

Hilton Mowbray   *c.£6,000*

Our client, a firm of business consultants based in Hilton Mowbray and established in 1986, now seek a Junior Secretary to assist the Research and Marketing Manager and provide secretarial support, word processing, administration and some reception duties. To be successful you will need:

- a minimum of one year's work experience within an office environment
- to be aged 17 - 20 with English and Maths GCSE's and RSA I and II (or equivalent) in typing or keyboard skills
- word processing experience in a Windows environment; Ami Pro would be an advantage
- to be of smart appearance, able to work neatly with a good telephone manner
- to be confident, conscientious, enthusiastic and keen to develop sound office skills

This position offers the opportunity to join a professional office providing a high standard of customer service and administration.

Please apply with a handwritten covering letter stating how you match the above requirements and a copy of your cv, quoting ref.887, to Sharon Teague, Longbow Consultants Limited, Norman House, 39 High Street, Hilton Mowbray HM13 8QT

LONGBOW
CONSULTANTS • LIMITED

H

JOB SHARE PART-TIME RECEPTIONIST

We are a well established property development company urgently seeking a smart, reliable and efficient receptionist for part-time duties (our reception is a non-smoking area).

Hours of work are 1.15 pm - 5.45 pm from Monday to Friday. Duties to include:-

★ Operating a Plessey Masterline Switchboard. Training will be given but the successful application will have reception/switchboard experience.

★ Typing to a good standard using Microsoft Word (training will be given on this system).

★ Some full-time work to cover holidays, etc.
Please apply in writing to:-
Melanie Carter, Central Homes Ltd, 144 Station Approach, Hilton Mowbray HM13 6RS

I

CATALOGUE DISTRIBUTORS

required by international food company to deliver 300 frozen food catalogues per week, to local homes, and to call back for orders for home delivery.

Earnings will be in the region of £250 commission, plus bonuses and discounts – all paid weekly!

For further details call Tim Andrews on **(01735) 403480**

eismann

Member of the Direct Selling Association

J

ASSISTANT PLAYGROUND LEADER

Required by Charteris Pre-School Playgroup.
For further information plus interview phone (01735) 510828

K

TRAINEE KENNEL HELP WANTED

Super job for someone who loves animals.
Two miles
Hilton Mowbray
Tel: 01735 261126

L

URGENTLY REQUIRED:

Part-time Catering Assistants

To work evenings & weekends in a busy fast food restaurant.

Experienced preferred but training will be given.

Please phone for an application form on: (01735) 366440

M

CAUGHT YOU LOOKING TIRED OF THE SAME OLD 9-5?

LOOKING TO IMPROVE?

Ace Food Distributors require 12 people to service Hilton Mowbray and surrounding areas.
We offer £600+ per week OTE (Commission + Bonus).

Company vehicle provided. Realistic advancement opportunities. Complete ongoing training.
No experience necessary. Must be 21+ years of age.

Contact Mr. Aziz for personal interview on
(01735) 445345

N

MOWBRAY HAIR + BEAUTY

are now recruiting for enthusiastic + ambitious
APPRENTICES + A PART TIME STYLIST
Excellent on going education + great career opportunities in a busy and exciting salon.
Why not telephone: 01735 711554

O

CAR VALETERS

required

For immediate start in Hilton Mowbray area
Top rates of pay for Valeters who must be fully experienced in new and used car preparation to the highest standard. Own transportation and ability to work on own initiative essential.

For details please ring Miss Blake
01735 560777

P

AQUA SPORT LTD

have a vacancy for

STORES ASSISTANT

to assist in a busy Stores Department. Ideally, candidates should have flexibility to work weekends and out of normal working hours.

Please apply in writing to:

Alan Chang
Aqua Sport Ltd
47 Missenden Road
Hilton Mowbray
HM14 2TT

Q

GARDENER/LABOURERS

FOR NEW CONTRACT

You should have experience in grass cutting (motor mowers), strimming, hedge cutting, bordering etc. etc. You must have your own safety footwear, all other safety wear/equipment is supplied.

DRIVING LICENCE ESSENTIAL
ALSO REQUIRED
TRIPLE/TRACTOR DRIVERS
Must be experienced.
Start date for the above will be staggered between now and the end of March. This temporary contract is expected to run until September/October.

Interested?
Please phone Ray Lear on:
01735 401620 (agy)

R

Part time
FOOT CANVASSERS

Basic + Bonus
£150 per week, earn full time money working part time hours as part of a team not home improvements, loans or finance
Call Ann on 01735 - 644585

S

CUSTOMER CARE ASSISTANT

We have a vacancy in our customer care department for someone who enjoys dealing with the public, has a basic knowledge of motor cars and is happy to work with computers. Full or part-time considered.

Please apply in writing to:
Patel & Sons (Hilton) Ltd
Station Concourse
Hilton Mowbray HM18 0RR

T

ACR

FULL TIME
CAR CLEANER / DRIVER

ACR Citroën, requires a person to prepare cars for delivery and deliver them to customers.

The position will ideally suit a smart active, semi-retired individual.

Call Hamira Khan
ACR Citroen
(01735) 647000

U

Back to Back Models
£65 - £75 per day

Male and Female Fashion Catwalk Models required for a prestigous client, for several bookings throughout the year. Requirements 25 - 35yrs
Minimum 5' 7" Female or 5' 11" Male with a confident personality. Choreography tuition can be taught to the inexperienced. We are still looking for Exhibition Personnel
18 yrs plus (£55 - £120 per day)
Ask for extension 765
Arcadia are looking for personnel to employ for MODEL/EXHIBITION assignments also Temp/Permanent staff in Administration Secretarial - Middle Management - Computer Accounting - Media - P.R. & Marketing
Send C.V. with Photo to:
Arcadia Exhibitions, 17-20 Victoria Avenue, Hilton Mowbray HM17 6CF

V

PLAYWORKERS

Austin Rd out of school project is an Activity Centre that caters for children after school and during school holidays. We are looking for an enthusiastic person to join us, preferably over 21 with transport.

You will be required to pick children up from school and ensure they have lots of fun by joining in with painting, cooking and playing games etc.

Salary to be arranged.
IF YOU WOULD LIKE TO FIND OUT MORE PLEASE CONTACT GEETA NAZIR ON 375644 BETWEEN 4-6PM

4 What can you expect to earn if you got a job by calling:

(a) Mike Young? [ ]

(d) Tim Andrews? [ ]

(b) Ann? [ ]

(e) Mr Aziz? [ ]

(c) Sharon Teague? [ ]

5 Write down the letter of the advertisement panel you would look at if you wanted a job:

(a) with children [ ]

(f) as a model [ ]

(b) in catering [ ]

(g) with computers [ ]

(c) in the motor trade [ ]

(h) working out of doors [ ]

(d) as a receptionist [ ]

(i) which helped you keep fit [ ]

(e) in hairdressing [ ]

(j) with animals [ ]

6 Write down the letter of the advertisements which require:

(a) experience in grass cutting [ ]

(b) flexibility to work weekends [ ]

(c) six month sales experience [ ]

(d) switchboard experience [ ]

(e) a confident personality [ ]

(f) excellent telephone manner [ ]

(g) a good sense of humour [ ]

(h) an enthusiastic, smart person [ ]

(i) word processing experience in a Windows environment [ ]

(j) basic knowledge of motor cars [ ]

7 Which of the jobs advertised are part-time?

[ ] [ ] [ ] [ ] [ ] [ ] [ ] [ ]

8 Which jobs require you to provide your own transport? [ ]

9 Which job will provide you with a company vehicle? ☐

10 Which of the jobs advertised would suit the following kinds of people?

(*a*) students ☐   (*d*) age 21+ ☐

(*b*) age 17-20 ☐   (*e*) semi-retired ☐

(*c*) age 18 years and over ☐

11 Which advertisement gives a freephone number? ☐

12 Ace Food Distributors offer earnings of £600+ per week **OTE**. This means 'on-target earnings' and means you can earn this much if you are successful. But if you are not a natural salesperson, you might earn a great deal less!

   Which advertisement offers the highest OTE earnings? ☐

13 To work weekly earnings out as an annual salary, you need to multiply the weekly earnings by 52.

So £200 per week would be £10,400 per year (£200 x 52).

How much would you expect to earn each year if you got a job as a:

(*a*) foot canvasser? ☐

(*b*) catalogue distributor? ☐

(*c*) service agent for Ace Food Distributors? ☐

14 On a separate sheet of paper, put together your own CV.

You might want to set it out in the format shown on sheet 41•6.

15 Pick one of the job advertisements and write a letter of application which sets out why you think you would be the most suitable person for the job. Attach your CV. Discuss your application and CV with others in your group.

CURRICULUM VITAE

NAME:

ADDRESS:

TELEPHONE:

DATE OF BIRTH: AGE:

NATIONALITY:

STATUS (MARRIED OR SINGLE):

DRIVING LICENCE:

EDUCATIONAL QUALIFICATIONS

School/College	Examinations year	Qualifications gained

EMPLOYMENT HISTORY

Year started	Employer	Brief description of job (main duties and experience)

OTHER RELEVANT EXPERIENCE

Details of hobbies, interests, leisure pursuits which demonstrate personal qualities.
Note any particular achievements.

REFEREES

Names and addresses of two people who can provide a
written reference for you.

Answers to exercises

1 Everyday signs

1 Answers in any order:

- woman smoking in 'no smoking' area
- person walking up right-hand staircase, despite 'keep left' direction sign
- person opening 'No entry' door
- man going into the 'Ladies'!
- buggy on escalator, despite prohibition sign
- person standing on left of escalator, despite 'stand on right' sign
- shopping trolley parked in front of 'Fire Exit - Please keep clear' sign
- cyclist on footpath
- car parked on double yellow lines
- person crossing road, despite 'Don't cross' sign on Pelican crossing

2 (a) parking
  (b) tourist information
  (c) telephone
  (d) railway station
  (e) roadworks
  (f) footpath
  (g) no waiting
  (h) bus stop
  (i) disabled toilets
  (j) keep right

2 How much electricity do you use?

1. 1
2. 2
3. 10
4. 1
5. ½
6. 2 hours
7. 20 minutes
8. 30 minutes
9. 60 minutes
10. 5 hours

3 Reading an electricity meter

	Units used	Night units cost	Day units cost
1.	618	£22.25	£57.16
2.	1217	£43.81	£112.57
3.	1566	£56.38	£144.86
4.	3293	£118.55	£304.60
5.	1313	£42.27	£121.45

6. 6
7. 2
8. 7
9. 4
10. 56,328
11. 42,735
12. 23,487

4 Shopping from a catalogue

1. 11
2. 6

	Lowest	Highest
3.	£14.90	£39.00

4. £24.10

5. (a) 421/6357
   (b) 421/5303
   (c) 421/5286
   (d) 421/2784
   (e) 421/5303

6. Own choice: could be any of
   421/6333
   421/6340
   421/5822

7. Check for reasoning. Could be that 'microchip browning control' makes the toaster sound very high-tech and therefore attractive. (It probably isn't a very big advance on the 'electronic' browning control on the other toasters.)

8. • Mid-cycle reheat button
   • Integral bun/croissant warming rack
   • Safety jam proof switch off
   • Slide out crumb tray

9. Check for reasoning. Toaster chosen can be anything up to £30 in price, with most features for the money. Student is asked to explain why he/she selected the particular toaster.

5 Using a telephone directory

1. P
2. B
3. E
4. W
5. C
6. H
7. D
8. L
9. A
10. G
11. H
12. R

13. (a) 0800 887766 or 0800 828282
    (b) 0800 800500
    (c) 0800 1111

14. The Speaking Clock

15. (a) 01296 396000   (b) 999

16. 0171 487 3000

17. Martin, Mead

18. (a) Chapelton 390506
    (b) Manfield 671884
    (c) Stanford 872403
    (d) Manfield 671005
    (e) Chapelton 390463
    (f) Chapelton 390521

19. (a) D. Merrett
    (b) Roy Marsden
    (c) C. Mason
    (d) D. Madden

20. J.H. Martin and D. Merrett

21. Martin Auto Repairs, Master Class Instruments Ltd, Maynard & Thursby, Mead Carpets Ltd, Mercers Stores

22. (a) Manfield 671344
    (b) Ifield 541306
    (c) Manfield 671005

23. (a) Brady, M.L.
    (b) Evans, Ann
    (c) Davis, Dr C.
    (d) Coach and Horses, The

24. (a) Mellor, R.S.
    (b) Meals on Wheels
    (c) Madden, D.

25. Enter the local telephone numbers of the people listed:
    (a)
    (b)
    (c)
    (d)
    (e)
    (f)
    (g)
    (h)
    (i)
    (j)

6   Yellow Pages 1

1. (a) 594   (d) 596
   (b) 494   (e) 608
   (c) 608

2. (a) building societies   (d) organ dealers
   (b) toy and game shops   (e) domestic services
   (c) boat hire

3. music

4. (a) hotels and inns
   (b) places of worship
   (c) toilets - portable

5. (a) entertainers 364
   (b) toy and game shops 899
   (c) music teachers 606

Enter the subjects listed in local edition of *Yellow Pages*:

6.   9.
7.   10.
8.

7   Yellow Pages 2

1. 3

2. Each new section-heading starts with a highlighted 'banner' with the *Yellow Pages* logo.

3. The *Yellow Pages* 'walking fingers' logo

4. (a) guide words
   (b) music, musical instrument

5. (a) Music arrangers and composers
   (b) Musical instrument and music shops
   (c) Musical instrument accessories
   (d) Musical instrument manufacturers and wholesalers
   (e) Music schools

6. (a) Resist Promotions   (d) Beecher Acoustics Oxford
   (b) The Drum Pad   (e) Noel Holburn
   (c) Alec Leader Keyboards

7. (a) David Snelling Violins
   (b) Alec Leader Keyboards
   (c) Drum Clinic or The Drum Pad

8. (a) Letchworth 482466   (d) Dunstable 605670
   (b) Bedford 750515   (e) Milton Keynes 370285
   (c) Turvey 881777

8   Yellow Pages 3

Enter answers which relate to your local edition of *Yellow Pages* and the telephone directory. Some good discussion opportunities here - don't lose them!

1.   8.
2.   9.
3.   10.
4.   11.
5.   12.
6.   13.
7.

9   BT national telephone charges

1. (a) Monday - Friday 8.00 am - 6.00 pm
   (b) Monday - Friday 8.00 am - 6.00 pm
   (c) Monday - Friday 6.00 pm - 8.00 am
   (d) All day Saturday and Sunday
   (e) Monday - Friday 9.00 am - 1.00 pm

2. a, b1, b

3. Weekend, Cheap, Daytime

4. Cheap, Standard, Peak

5. (a) 80 seconds   (d) 25.60 seconds
   (b) 90 seconds   (e) 7.61 seconds
   (c) 50.35 seconds

6. least/lowest

7. A call to an information service at Cheap rate is the most expensive call

8. (a) 10 hours   (d) 6 hours
   (b) 24 hours   (e) 14 hours
   (c) 4 hours

9. Saturday and Sunday

10. (a) 15p   (d) £1.49
    (b) 40p   (e) 90p
    (c) £1.58

10   Dialling codes

1. Alphabetical order

2. (a) 01653   (d) 01455
   (b) 01746   (e) 01433
   (c) 01482

3. (a) Hindon   (d) High Wycombe
   (b) Hubberts Bridge   (e) Hornsea
   (c) Hook Norton

4. (a) Hitchin   (d) Hindon
   (b) Hilderstone   (e) Howden
   (c) Horwich

5. (a) a   (d) a
   (b) b   (e) L
   (c) b

11   Telephone bills

1. 216   £9.072

2. Hilton Mowbray (01735) 682927

3. HK 2644 8389 J018 S3

4. 22 December

5. £101.05

6. (a) 6   (c) 2
   (b) 3

7. (a) 29 October   (c) 10 December
   (b) 28 November   (d) 28 November

8. Horsham

9. It was a local call

10. Check for reasons given to support each ticked box:
    (a), (b), (d), (f), (g), (h)

12 International telephone charges

1. 8, Republic of Ireland

2. Canada, USA

3. Singapore

4. (a) 5   (d) 1
   (b) 2   (e) 3
   (c) 6

5. (a) Standard   (d) Cheap
   (b) Standard   (e) Cheap
   (c) Cheap

6. (a) 5.82 seconds   (d) 4.40 seconds
   (b) 4.50 seconds   (e) 6.35 seconds
   (c) 10.00 seconds

13 At the sandwich bar

1.
2 x cheese	1.60
2 x toasted cheese	2.00
3 x bacon	1.80
2 x ham	1.60
1 x toasted ham	1.00
1 x sausage	0.60
3 x salad	2.10
2 x large tea	1.00
1 x small tea	0.40
2 x large coffee	1.60
1 x small coffee	0.50
Total	**£14.20**

2. Reg and Neema have given you the wrong money.

3. Because they wanted *toasted* sandwiches, which cost extra.

14 At the café

1. Check four main menu headings filled in: main courses, side orders, desserts, drinks.

2. A snack and a drink up to the value of £2.50. Check arithmetic!

3. Own choice of food/drink. Check bill total. Check change from £10.

4. A 'healthy' meal and drink. Check bill total. Check change from £10.

5. (a) *Christos*
sausage & chips	1.80
beans	0.40
mushrooms	0.50
bread	0.20
chocolate sponge	0.80
2 large teas	1.00
Total	£4.70

Tracey
vegetable curry	3.50
extra fried rice	0.95
chappati	0.30
naan bread	0.40
fruit pie	0.80
Coke	0.60
Total	£6.55

You
lasagne	2.80
2 poppadoms	0.40
mineral water	0.50
small coffee	0.50
Total	£4.20

(b) £4.55

(c) You get 80p change. Christos gets 30p change.

15 Food shopping

1. List of evening meals and weekend lunches.

2. Shopping list based on No. 1 above.

3. Total of shopping bill (refer to food display for prices).

4. (a) No
   (b) You bought only 2 packets of brown rice and 1 bag of frozen peas. But you had 3 wholemeal loaves in your trolley: only 2 have appeared on the bill.
   (c) £17.55

16 A theatre seating plan

1. They have the closest view of the stage.

2. Sidestage; because you only get a 'side-on' view.

3. Because you get four seats for £16.50.

4. (a) A5, A6   (d) A and D
   (b) A18, A19   (e) E1, E36
   (c) C1, C18

5. (a) £16.50   (f) (6 x £6.10) plus
   (b) £25.50   (6 x £5.90) = £36.60 +£35.40
   (c) £36   = £72   less 20% on 6 stalls
   (d) £35.20   seats (£7.32)
   (e) £22.90   £72 - £7.32 = £64.68
                   (g) £29.75

6. Stalls seat L10.

7. (a) E3 and E4
   (b) 60p more per seat (or 30p more per seat if Aisha and Claire are children).

8. In stalls rows K or L.

9.
Adults: Stalls row B and C: 26 seats x £9.10 =	£236.60
Sidestage: 9 seats x £5.90 =	£53.10
Children: Stalls row A: 10 seats x £9.10 x ½ price =	£45.50
Total:	£335.20
Less 20% of stalls rows B, C and A ([£236.60 + £45.50] x 20%)	£56.42
Net Total:	£278.78

10. (a)
Boxes 4 x 4	16
Sidestage 3 x 18	54
Circle 5 x 36	180
Stalls A-C	36
Stalls D-L 9 x 16	144
Total number of seats	430

(b) Total box-office takings were as follows:
Boxes	4 x £16.50	66.00
Sidestage	54 x £5.90	318.60
Circle A-C	108 x £8.50	918.00
Circle D-E	72 x £7.20	518.40
Stalls A-E	68 x £9.10	618.80
Stalls F-J	80 x £8.50	680.00
Stalls K-L	32 x £6.10	195.20
	Total:	£3,315.00

17 Getting organised

1. (a) Monday 14 May
   (b) Sunday 20 May
   (c) 7

2. The 20th week of the year, counting from 1 January.

3. (a) 8.15 am
   (b) 8.00 pm

4. (a) A/309
   (b) A/406
   (c) A/642

5. (a) Because it's the start of a new week of activity.
   (b) Because the health and safety inspection happened on Thursday.

6. Tuesday or Thursday.

7. (a) 1 hour 45 minutes
   (b) 2 hours 30 minutes

8. (a) 2 hours 15 minutes
   (b) 5.45 pm

9. Wednesday morning and Thursday afternoon.

10. (a) Tuesday
    (b) Technics UK (marketing team)

11. French class, Amnesty (International)

12. Because the owner of the diary is collecting Yussuf's birthday cake on Friday.

13. It's the diary owner's anniversary.

14. Could be either. The temptation is to assume that the owner of the organiser is a man, because he/she is in business - some useful discussion should arise!

18 Using the *Radio Times*

1. (a) 5.35 pm   (c) 5.40 pm
   (b) 5.30 pm   (d) 5.50 pm

2. (a) Six O'Clock News
   (b) *Star Trek: The Next Generation*
   (c) *Home and Away*
   (d) *The Crystal Maze*

3. 5

4. (a) *Coronation Street* (7.30)
   (b) BBC2

5. Pages 52-6

6. (a) 6.00 (9.00)
   (b) 10.30
   (c) 5.40 (10.00)
   (d) 7.00

7. 5.35   *Neighbours*   BBC1
   6.00   *Home and Away*   ITV
   7.30   *Coronation Street*   ITV
   8.00   *Brookside*   Channel 4

8. (a) *Points of View*
   (b) *Rhodes around Britain*
   (c) *Sportsnight* (or *Natural Born Footballers*)
   (d) *Moviewatch*
   (e) *Star Trek: The Next Generation*
   (f) *University Challenge* (or *Talking Telephone Numbers*)
   (g) *Rhodes around Britain* (or *Travelog*)
   (h) *Des O'Connor Tonight* (or *This is Your Life*)

9. (a) *Winter in Wales*
   (b) *Dirty Dozen: The Fatal Mission*
   (c) Regional News

10. (a) 1 hour   (d) 15 minutes
    (b) 30 minutes   (e) 50 minutes
    (c) 1 hour 40 minutes (f) 45 minutes

11. (a) David Attenborough
    (b) Anne Robinson
    (c) Alison Holloway
    (d) Fintan O'Toole
    (e) Desmond Lynam

12. (a) Vivien Kent   (e) Patrick Stewart
    (b) Peter Batty   (f) Malcolm Morris
    (c) Anna Ford   (g) Jenny Mallinson Duff
    (d) Leonard Nimoy   (h) Susan Pleat

19 Using Teletext

1. (a) 123   (d) 141-148
   (b) 112   (e) 208-209
   (c) 300

2. (a) 119   (d) 192
   (b) 328   (e) 218
   (c) 104

3. Answers will vary from day to day.
   (b) Look at Flashback on page 671.

20   Which bus goes where?

1. (a) 40, 41   (d) 65
   (b) 44   (e) 48A, 53A
   (c) 44, 48   (f) 42, 42A

2. Market Street

3. Southampton Road and Bishopstoke Road

4. (a) 66   (d) 42, 42A
   (b) 69, 69A   (e) 62
   (c) 48, 69   (f) 49

5. (a) under   (c) under
   (b) over   (d) under

6. (a) 49   (d) 65
   (b) 65   (e) 49
   (c) 47

21   Planning a bus journey

1. (a) Allbrook Hill
   (b) Spring Lane
   (c) Saint Cross Road

2. Not Saturdays

3. Saturdays only

4. (a) 0617   (d) 2232
   (b) 0920   (e) Colden Common
   (c) 0717

5. (a) 44   (b) 0826

6. Hiltingbury

7. (a) 5   (b) every 2 hours

8. 2251

9. 1120

10. 38 minutes

11. Route Planner

From	Bus	Leave at	To	Arrive at
Eastleigh	41	0932	Hiltingbury	0952
Hiltingbury	40	1238	Eastleigh	1258
Eastleigh	44	1432	Winchester	1510
Winchester	44	1720	Eastleigh	1758

22   Using the 24-hour clock

1. 3.00 pm   11. 0500
2. 4.00 pm   12. 1700
3. 2.30 pm   13. 1430
4. 4.30 pm   14. 0100
5. 6.00 pm   15. 1940
6. 3.40 am   16. 0730
7. 10.30 am   17. 1355
8. 6.00 am   18. 0905
9. 6.45 pm   19. 2330
10. 10.20pm   20. 1615

23   Which train shall I catch?

1. (a) 156   (d) 150
   (b) 181   (e) 156, 182
   (c) 182   (f) 167

2. 406

3. (a) Bank
   (b) Kensington Olympia, Clapham Junction

4. Water (The Solent)

5. (a) 14   (e) 206
   (b) 600   (f) 133
   (c) 1   (g) 158
   (d) 64   (h) 158

6. Basingstoke

7. Yes

8. Yes; there is a star in the catering column for Aylesbury.

9. Basingstoke, Bath Spa

10. (a) Yes   (d) No
    (b) No   (e) No
    (c) Yes   (f) Yes

11. Balham, Bank, Barking

12. Bayford

13. (a) Yes   (d) Yes
    (b) No   (e) No
    (c) Yes   (f) Yes

14. Yes

15. Barnhill

24   Planning a rail journey

1. (a) 0545   (d) 0658
   (b) 0751   (e) 0710
   (c) 2 hours 6 minutes   (f) 12 minutes

2. (a) 0702   (c) 1 hour 34 minutes
   (b) 0836   (d) 15 minutes longer

3. (a) 1 hour 38 minutes   (b) 28 minutes faster

4. (a) 0001   (d) 3 hours 44 minutes
   (b) London Waterloo   (e) It waits in Southampton
   (c) 0345   for 31 minutes

5 The 0654

6 0650

7 Weymouth

8. Derby, 0600

9. The 0708

10.

From	To	Depart (time)	Train timetable number	Arrive (time)
1 Southampton	Basingstoke	0813	158	0856
2 Basingstoke	Salisbury	0958	145	1039
3 Salisbury	Romsey	1644	165	1709
4 Romsey	Southampton	1909	165	1922

25 AA Handbook

1. (a) Technical services   (d) Travelling abroad
   (b) Accidents   (e) Help for drivers with
   (c) Books and maps   disabilities

2. (a) 22   (d) 8
   (b) 11   (e) 22
   (c) 94

3. (a) 15   (d) 30
   (b) 23   (e) 25
   (c) 16

4. 60

5. Motorways

26 Using the *AA Handbook* Road Atlas key

1. 61

2. (a) 48   (d) 49
   (b) 12, 13   (e) 26
   (c) 47

3. The Isle of Man

4. South

5. p.3

6. p.4

7. Kirkwall

8. Liverpool

9. They have AA Service Centres

10. (a) p.11   (f) pp.8-9
    (b) p.4   (g) p.57
    (c) p.15   (h) p.23
    (d) p.29   (i) p.55
    (e) p.34   (j) p.18

27 Using a road atlas

1. Norwich

2. Norfolk

3. The Wash

4. East

5. (a) The A12
   (b) 10 miles
   (c) South

6. (a) 16 miles   (e) 9 miles
   (b) 9 miles   (f) 12 miles
   (c) 15 miles   (g) 14 miles
   (d) 12 miles   (h) 20 miles

7. Add two mileages together

8. (a) A11   (e) A10
   (b) A1116   (f) B1145
   (c) A47   (g) A148
   (d) A149

9. Great Ouse

10. A140, A148, A1067; 72 miles

11. (a) TG33   (d) TF60
    (b) TG24   (e) TM49
    (c) TF62

12. (a) Wymondham (e) New Buckenham (i) Long Stratton
    (b) Acle   (f) Swaffham   (j) Fakenham
    (c) Feltwell   (g) Stoke Ferry
    (d) Dereham   (h) Hunstanton

Answer to extra question from roadside picture: You are standing just south of Norwich on the A140.

28 Using a gazetteer

1. (a) Chatham
   (b) Chale, IOW

2. (a) Kent   (d) Lancashire
   (b) Gloucestershire   (e) Hampshire
   (c) Oxfordshire

3. (a) 7 SU 39   (c) 25 SK 94
   (b) 11 TQ 76   (d) 41 NZ 61

4. (a) Chagford, Chapel Cleeve

5. (a) Wednesday   (c) Thursday
   (b) Wednesday   (d) Wednesday

6. Chard, Saturday

7. (a) 7 miles   (c) 145 miles
   (b) 20 miles   (d) 4 miles

8. (a) Chadlington 437   (d) Charlbury 278
   (b) Charmouth 60319   (e) Brimscombe 3555
   (c) Chagford 3469

9. (a) 2
   (b) 15
   (c) 21
   (d) Greenacres
   (e) Great Tree, Mill End and Easton Court
   (f) Devon
   (g) The Bell and Charmouth House
   (h) Sea Horse Hotel
   (i) Chagford, Charmouth; more tourism

10. (a) Chadwell Heath, Chandler's Ford, Chartham,
        Chatham
    (b) 21.00
    (c) Goodmayes Motors Ltd
    (d) Caythorpe Motors and Charmouth Motors. They
        may be new garages or under new management.

29 Motorway route planner

1. straight, top, bottom

2. Junctions 7-13

3. (a) 1 mile   (d) 3 miles
   (b) 5 miles   (e) 5 miles
   (c) 2 miles   (f) 7 miles

4. 46 minutes

5. (a) A505
   (b) Dunstable
   (c) 2 miles

6. (a) A421   (d) Junction 10
   (b) Junction 13   (e) 28$\frac{1}{2}$ miles
   (c) 15 miles

7. (a) Junction 7   (d) 25 miles
   (b) 10 miles   (e) 30 minutes
   (c) Toddington

31 Flying out

1. (a) 3   (b) 3   (c) 2

2. Monday, Wednesday

3. Tuesday

4. (a) Luton, Manchester
   (b) Heathrow

5. (a) British Airways   (b) KLM

6. Air India

7. (a) Wednesday
   (b) Friday
   (c) Monday

8. (a) Manchester
   (b) Heathrow

30 Planning a road journey

Answers consist of a weekend diary (open-ended) and a route plan of the journey. Check for exact details of distance, road numbers and place names. This is the completed suggested route planner:

From	Road used	To	Distance (miles)	Hotel names	Garages/ Service Centres
Oxford	A40	Burford	22	–	–
Burford	A361	Lechlade	9	Not known	–
Lechlade	A417	Cirencester	13	Stratton House Hotel	–
Cirencester	A429	Northleach	10	–	–
Northleach	A429	Bourton-on-the-Water	5 (estimate)	Old New Inn	–
Bourton-on-the-Water	A429	Stow-on-the-Wold	4 (estimate)	–	–
Stow-on-the-Wold	A424	Broadway	10	Broadway Hotel	–
Broadway	A46/ B4077	Stow-on-the-Wold	Not known	Stow Lodge Hotel	Gloucester AA Centre (Glos.23278)
Stow-on-the-Wold	A436/ A44	Chipping Norton	Not known	–	E.C. Automotive, Chipping Norton
Chipping Norton	A34	Oxford	20	–	–

32 What's the weather like?

1. (a) sunny intervals
   (b) rain
   (c) overcast

2. (a) SE, 10 mph
   (b) S, 25 mph
   (c) SE, 20 mph

3. (a) 28 °C
   (b) 21 °C
   (c) 18 °C or 19 °C
   (d) 27 °C
   (e) 25 °C
   (f) 25 °C

4. cooler, wetter

5. the temperatures

6. dry, bright

7. Northern Ireland, Western Scotland

8. 6

9. (a) 1
   (b) 6

10. 1 and 2

11. (a) Worse   (b) Outlook

12. (a) Fishguard
    (b) Cromer
    (c) Bournemouth

13. (a) sun
    (b) rain
    (c) bright
    (d) cloud

14. (a) 3.2 hours
    (b) 0.4 hours
    (c) 3.4 hours

15. (a) 8 °C, 14 °F
    (b) 5 °C, 9 °F
    (c) 6 °C, 10 °F

33 How much will my holiday cost?

1. 500m

2. Platanias

3. Giorgos, Tula, Stratis and Anna

4. Troulakis

5. 10 km

6. Directly opposite the apartments

7. (a) 2: lounge/bedroom, bathroom
   (b) 3: lounge/dining room, bathroom, bedroom
   (c) 4: lounge/diner, bathroom, 2 bedrooms

8. (a) 2   (b) 3   (c) 5

9. (a) studio
   (b) one bedroom apartment
   (c) two bedroom apartment

10. (a) £398   (d) £324
    (b) £348   (e) £348
    (c) £474

11. (a) Tuesday   (c) Gatwick
    (b) Hania   (d) 1.05 pm

12. Total cost :   £868
                          £736
                          £1,272

13.
(a) 1 x £398 =   £398
    Plus supplement
    2 x £85   £170
    Total   £568

(c) 4 x £288 =   £1,152
    Less reduction
    1 x £70   £70
    Total   £1,082

(b) 3 x £444 = £1,332
    Less reduction
    2 x £70   £140
    Total   £1,192

(d) 1 x £484 =   £484
    Plus supplement
    2 x £90   £180
    Total   £664

34 Changing your money

1. (a) Dirham, 13.8474   (d) US$, 1.5649
   (b) Drachma, 372.747   (e) Franc, 8.2875
   (c) Peseta, 207.476   (f) Mauritius Rupee, 28.0901

2. (a) Ireland   (d) Finland
   (b) Thailand   (e) Tunisia
   (c) Austria   (f) Russia

3. Cyprus, Malta

4. Turkish Lira

5. Ireland

6. (a) Yuan, 660.245   (d) US$, 78.245
   (b) Rupee, 3904.305   (e) Maltese Lira, 28.67
   (c) Shekel, 253.89

7. (a) 7p   (d) 0.5p
   (b) 16p   (e) 19p
   (c) 6p   (f) 25p

8. (a) £47.54   (f) £3.23
   (b) £4.22   (g) £10.60
   (c) £4.05   (h) £10.20
   (d) £10.18   (i) £2.89
   (e) £1.74   (j) £1.20

35 Small ads

1. (a) very good condition
   (b) or near offer
   (c) evenings

2. (a) 0171 203 5881   (f) 0181 925 3524
   (b) 0181 375 8099   (g) 01280 73924
   (c) 0181 664 8993   (h) 0171 886 5092
   (d) 0171 556 6273 or   (i) 0181 435 8122
       0181 375 8099   (j) 0171 503 7764
   (e) 0181 765 2093

3. satellite system

4. the Metro City

5. knitting machine

6. satellite system

7. camcorder

8. golf clubs, vacuum cleaner

9. JVC PC70 portable stereo

36 VAT

1. £16.69   9. £7.39
2. £6.20   10. £387.09
3. £12.42   11. £169.36
4. £36.30   12. £15.14
5. £1,136.63   13. £29.15
6. £52.86   14. £212.76
7. £98.61   15. £680.84
8. £37.30   16. £76.59

37 Discounts

1. £1795.50
2. £2796
3. £4219.60
4. £2035.75
5. £2759.08

38 Personal banking: Budget Account

1. £205

2.

		Annual cost(£)
Budget Account charges	£2 per month x 12	24
Rent	£120 per week x 52	6,240
Council Tax	10 instalments of £33	330
Electricity	£4.50 per week x 52	234
Telephone	£60 per quarter x 4	240
Water Rates	£290 per year	290
Life Insurance	£225 per year	225
Home contents insurance	£47 per year	47
Monthly travel pass	£35 per month x 12	420
TV licence	£93 per year	93
Clothes	£250 per year	250
Household items	£250 per year	250
Total annual cost		£8,643

3. £720.25

4. £166.21

5. (a) £38.79   (b) (£205 - £166.21) = £38.79

6. (a) £10
   (b) £7.50
   (c) £390

7. (a) £8,988
   (b) £749

39 Personal banking: bank statements

1. (a) 2873994
   (b) 2642866

2. (a) Boyds Bank
   (b) 20-17-98

3. £534.32

4. £794.33

5. From current a/c 2642866   £749.00

6. 6 Dec   PLANET HOLLYWOOD MRCHD   £23.98
            LONDON W1

7. (a) 17 December   (c) 7 December
   (b) 9 December

8. (a) Courts Superstore   £96.36
   (b) Books Etc   £18.45
   (c) Cauldwell BC   £33.00

9. (a) milk bill
   (b) food shopping
   (c) books

40 Buying a car

	MAKE	MODEL
1.	Fiat	Cinquecento
	Lada	Samara 1.3S
	Rover	111i
	Peugeot	106 'Plus'

2. (a) Peugeot 106   (b) Lada Samara 1.3S

3. AGL Motors, Mount Rise Autos

4. (a) Crawfords
   (b) AGL Motors
   (c) Super Cars
   (d) Mount Rise Autos
   (e) AGL Motors

5. (a) Rover 111i
   (b) Fiat Cinquecento
   (c) Lada Samara

6. (a) 1.3 l
   (b) 1.1 l
   (c) 1.2 l

7. (a) 3 year manufacturer's warranty
   (b) 2 year/50,000 miles warranty
       6 year bodywork warranty
   (c) 6 year anti-corrosion warranty
       3 year cosmetic/paint warranty

8. Crawfords

9. (a) Because it spreads the cost over 4 years and you
       don't pay any extra interest
   (b) £164.58 per month
   (c) 4 years

10. (a) £6,295
    (b) £4,495
    (c) £6,599.20
    (d) £7,749

11. Five main reasons for choosing one car rather than
    another: good discussion opportunity

12. The car which offers best value for money (probably the
    Samara).

41 Looking for a job

1. 22

2. (a) O   (d) N
   (b) E   (e) B
   (c) T   (f) K

3. (a) Alan Chang   (d) Andy Scott
   (b) Mr Archer   (e) Hamira Khan
   (c) Geeta Nazir

4. (a) £800 p/week (£40,000 a year)
   (b) £150 p/week
   (c) £6,000
   (d) £250 plus bonuses/discounts
   (e) £600 p/week

5. (a) J or V   (f) U
   (b) A, F or L   (g) D, G or H
   (c) O or T   (h) I, Q or R
   (d) H   (i) B or Q
   (e) W   (j) K

6. (a) Q   (f) D
   (b) P   (g) F
   (c) E   (h) B
   (d) H   (i) G
   (e) U   (j) S

7. A, D, F, H, L, N, R, S, U, V

8. C, V

9. M

10. (a) D   (d) M
    (b) G   (e) T
    (c) A

11. C

12. C

13. (a) £7,800
    (b) £13,000
    (c) £31,200

14. Own CV. Check and discuss layout and content.
    Deciding what experience is relevant is sometimes
    tricky, and the CV should be concise and to the point.

15. Letter of application for one of the jobs. An ideal small-
    group discussion opportunity!